PLAYING WITH FIRE

A Year of Love Letters & Poems, Set Ablaze,
and Other Vulgar Lore Dedicated To You

PLAYING WITH FIRE

A Year of Love Letters & Poems, Set Ablaze,
and Other Vulgar Lore Dedicated To You

TEGAN MATTHEWS

300 SOUTH MEDIA GROUP

NEW YORK

PLAYING WITH FIRE

ISBN-13: 978-1-957596-22-8 (paperback)
ISBN-13: 978-1-957596-23-5 (ebook)

First Printing December 2023

Cover & Interior Design by Indie Author Solutions
Published by 300 South Media Group

This book is for all of the "YOUS" in the world who need to be seen and heard.

Table of Contents

Author's Note ~

I am a poet and writer; a creator and artist, bringing to life a world that lives within me. I have visualized and inked a world on these pages for you to now enjoy, see, live, experience, connect with, and feel.

The following has grown and developed throughout my life. I often felt like an impostor, my true self trapped within the confines of unknown skin, never feeling comfortable, always hiding the real me ~ who I was on the inside. I longed to be myself and never gave up hope of becoming who I was always meant to be, someone I did not let others freely see.

For many years, I often fought against the flow of society but still chose to swim along with everyone else until I couldn't take it anymore. I acknowledged I was selling myself short and finally ready to accept who I am becoming and to embrace life very differently - truly being my authentic self while creating a legacy.

I began writing poetry about love, loss, regret, trials, and tribulations along the way to process my decisions and actions under the premise of TGN poetry, the gorgeous nothing. More recently, I have been writing erotic poetry, diving into short stories, and working on my first fiction novel.

Living right outside Philadelphia, Pennsylvania, I've had many city adventures and some not-so-city adventures. Most of my writings and poems are about small moments that have taken place throughout my life. They have helped me accept and come to terms with who I am ~ my evolution and life storage, as you will.

My writing is also focused on capturing moments I have experienced, memories that pushed me and developed who I am today, mixed with a little bit of fiction and, of course, flair to add a bit of excitement along the way.

The poems included in this anthology are a collection of love letters written throughout the year to showcase the highs and lows of any relationship, feelings somewhat extreme at times, and desires lingering just below the surface. This journey is coming from a place of want ~ waiting to be read, wanting to be unconditionally accepted, and diving into who we may become together or apart.

This is a poetic story told between the lines, the ink bled daily, within the pages of my soul to share the ups and downs of the greatest loves of the world and to create hope that one day, perhaps, I will not feel so alone.

The words in this story are me ~ authentic, raw, in the flesh, bleeding my heart and soul through this year ~ a year of love letters and poems to an unknown, could be anyone we chose or even a friend that holds your hand when feeling low. Hidden within these pages is a story of truth, love, heartache, longing, acceptance, rage, peace, understanding, and transformation.

Thank you for coming along with me through the first year of discovering who I am and building my future in crafting the love I deserve and desire.

Tegan Matthews

Introduction ~

I am an impostor, most times in my life. In the past. In the present.

I realized this devastating truth in quiet moments, sitting alone, observing others' interactions as time drains quickly through my slippery grasp. At times, I am unable to hold on to who I am while getting lost in thought of where I long to be, need to be, and perhaps where I am supposed to be ~ such as feeling the morning sun while having dessert in a Paris cafe with you, or laughing over cherry whiskey during the twilight hour in my backyard, sipping on whatever the poison and desire it is we have chosen to satiate ourselves today.

But still, I play the part I am meant to and choose to fulfill roles the world rationally expects of me. This daunting realization continues to be a never-ending curse as emotions endlessly swirl through my mind, merely surviving what the day births while I put my cravings to sleep. For when I wake, the harsh reality smacks me in the face yet again that it is me . . . who is the impostor ~

The impostor in this demanding, harsh world ~ always longing for what is to come while maintaining the facade of expectation. One that I have expertly crafted ~ a masterpiece, a perfected creation that everyone sees but does not really know the person behind the mask.

WINTER

Playing With Fire

The Beginning ~ Winter

Beginnings are always filled with magic and wonder, excitement and newness, intrigue and mystery. There is purity in this time of year, a fresh start, a rebirth. Winter is also filled with darkness and knowledge, perhaps receiving a needed education in all that is love and desire. This time of year is enchanting and, for me, full of salacious curiosity.

And so,
    the legacy and story begin . . .

"A writer writes. A feeler feels. A lover loves. But an arsonist, a poetess, well ~ she sets her world on fire just to watch it burn down to the ground all around her.

Only a few are brave enough to truly embrace their passions within themselves to take flight ~ uncaging pre-existing constraints and are courageous enough to risk it all. Passion is love and heartache. Passion is kindness and facing harsh truths. Passion is setting yourself on fire just to feel sometimes or relishing in the beauty around you.

Sometimes, as a result, you will harshly fall or weightlessly soar, but in doing so, you will finally unleash what is truly meant to be."

~ Tegan Matthews

Playing With Fire

December 21st ~
(the first letter I wrote to you)

To know me is to know moments remembered.
I have lived all these small moments in time,
and experienced greatness and pain
Every word inked on these pages to you
has left a mark and tells a story.
Remnants safely tucked away to experience,
and remember every detail forever.
every adventure, heartbreak, love, and joy,
lonely, invisible moments, and mistakes I made.
My writing is a testament to who I am...
parts of my life that created me,
and what I have learned throughout my days
breaking down shelves, opening curtains
unboxing compartments kept
to separate my life into neat piles
I open it all up to you ~ to see my soul,
and share the unknowns of me
Moments I share have been slammed together in truth ~
my life storage, as you will
Miles traveled to hunt down where I belong,
listening to my intuition, following my heart
to figure out who I am meant to be
in this lonely but crowded world
I look forward to our adventures
navigating our existence together
connecting in ways others cannot even fathom

December 22nd ~

When courage overtakes you, even for a moment,
follow that calling, embrace the strength that prevails
and relish in the freedom to be authentically you
Let the wind take you wildly dancing
confidently sailing through vivid visions
creating unforgettable moments
to show the world who you are destined to be
Letting go of boxed images is powerful, liberating
cathartic and validating
Thirty seconds ~ to make a decision
Thirty seconds ~ is all you need
to make yourself truly known

December 23rd ~

Yes, I'm waiting
I am waiting for you
to make the first move
I am endlessly waiting for you
to be tempted by my neverending
will and all-consuming energy
I am waiting for you
to be mine in every way
and waiting for you
to head south
to penetrate
my body and soul

December 24th ~

As we navigate and create a spontaneous path of uncertainty, pleasurable thoughts are mounting, and the thrill of what is to come is lingering, weighing heavily on my mind. I long for our first touch and enchanted moments to be actualized.

It is becoming abundantly evident that you ~ embody the child-like magic of Christmas Eve to me.

December 25th ~
(At the end of the most magical night, there was you)

The day was filled with delightful distractions, fun, wrapping, and excitement. Time was spent with family, and moments were treasured that are held deep within our hearts.

But, when all is quiet, my focus turns solely to you. We sit next to one another, cuddled and warm, reflecting on the day, the year, remembering every moment that brought us great joy and love; with me securely in your lap. Relishing in the silence, the sacredness of our connection, soaking in the last of the twinkling white lights on the tree, your scent, and the night ahead entwined in your embrace.

This, by far, is my favorite part of the day, the most magical ~ the last moments of Christmas night with you.

December 26th ~
(My life is simply better with you in it)

I love your presence in my world. I love how you hold my hand and wrap your arms around my body. I love the make-believe stories we imagine and create as we walk down the street laughing, entirely engrossed with one another. I love our adventures in the woods and how you make me feel as though I am flying. I love our morning phone calls and late-night texts and how we can talk endlessly about the days ahead or those that have already transpired. You inspire me never to settle and always be ready for fun surprises.

But I also love when the mood changes and settles, and we can just lay next to one another, snuggling, touching, and feeling your lips on the back of my neck, knowing you are learning to put another first and care about someone else's feelings aside from your own. I love that you think of me when I am not around and how you send me songs that remind you of me. I love that I have become a part of different facets of your separate worlds, and I have been accepted and infused into all. I love that you are willing to explore my body and my soul, never quite knowing what you are getting into, what I will spring on you next, and always being on edge with what I will say or do.

Thank you for being in my life. Our time in this world is so short, and some of the best moments in our lives may not have even happened yet. I love that we can experience moments together and fill our time in meaningful ways. Thank you for being you and authentically loving who I am, even if I may drive you to the brink of insanity at times.

9

December 27th ~

As the night ends,
I sit perched on my windowsill,
looking up,
gazing at thousands of stars,
thinking of you,
knowing you are with me
looking up at the same stars in the same sky
Tonight ~ I am wishing upon a star
for you to be mine

December 28th ~

I beg of you to kiss every part of my throbbing body. You damn well know what you do to me with your voice, your gentle touch, and your velvet lips.

I am anticipating your next move, the next message, the next time you are inches from me, passionately kissing my longing lips and fully claiming what is yours and has been yours from the very beginning of time.

December 29th ~

Our connection
was brought on
like a raging fire

explosive
dynamic
impenetrable

Over time, it continues
to grow, to be fed,
and in turn, we are
creating one of the
greatest love stories
of our time

December 30th ~

Take my hand, and I will walk alongside you on the grandest
adventure of our lives as we let go of every insecurity and
inhibition, we have ever had ~ Stay with me always,
rediscovering our magic together when lost or stagnant or
when we are both feeling alone and needy.

December 31st ~

Never before did I desire to be near another as I do with you
Evermore wanting to be caressed by your hands as well as
your mind
Wanting this new year to bring joy to us both, two
becoming one while

Yearning to be next to you, fully soaking in your presence
before me
Exquisite silk being draped around my body and tied around
my wrists
Arousing me completely, waiting for you to slowly bite my
neck to leave evidence of our night together, marking,
claiming me as yours
Righting every wrong at this moment while
Sensually feeling all emotions we share physically, at last

Earning my trust, you now have the ability and strength to
fulfill every desire you had during our time together, even
before meeting
Vampish appeal of mine becoming your reality and
Equally, embracing your domineering presence, giving in,
relinquishing control to let love seep into your soul finally
and forever fully

January 1st ~

Darkness dominates under the surface while illumination radiates from my eyes. I plead with myself over and over again to choose the light, but darkness exists deep in my soul, swallowing me whole.

Decisions made teetering on risqué, pushing the limits, a dare paired with overwhelmingly reckless nights, abandonment of all responsibilities; I am consumed by an all-encompassing blanket of emotion as the existence of unwelcomed lingering intensity surges uncontrollably through my veins.

Why does the light not excite me? Why can I not be satiated by blissful ignorance, ignoring the shadows that besiege my soul, swallowing my thoughts whole? Will there come a time when darkness becomes disinterested, not an inherent need?

Until that day arrives, the twilight of devilry calls out to me once again, and so I go.

January 2nd ~

I want you to notice me. I want you to accept me for who I am. I want you to acknowledge how much effort goes into making sure you are happy, how much effort goes into making sure you feel loved always and satisfied daily. I want you to take me in your arms again and remind me of your love. I want you to stay. I want you never to get enough of me, to never get enough of our conversations, and never get enough of touching my soul. I want you to look me in the eyes and allow me to see into your thoughts to get a first-hand glimpse of how you feel. I want you. I want us. I want it all, forever.

January 3rd ~

For a brief moment, I felt like Little Red Riding Hood, draped in white, being successfully seduced by the wolf himself. I was entranced by you standing before me, entirely consumed, and already was being quickly devoured when I realized what was about to transpire.

I couldn't shake the feeling that I had known you for a long time, but that was impossible; we just met last night. This was a fleeting thought racing through my mind. It was uncanny, though ~ it felt like you have been in my life, in some way, for years.

January 4th ~

Tell me ghost stories from your past. I want to understand and explore thoughts that run through your mind, what makes you - you, and where I eternally fit in. I want to take up residence in the dark places of your soul to either sit with you in despair, keeping the company of your demons or providing the light, to brighten the path out of turmoil, guiding your hand, and being the sign you need that everything will eventually be okay.

January 5th ~
(What are your deepest, darkest desires in life?)

There's always a climax in your story, a moment that defines you. How you choose to move on from that is key. Does it propel you forward? Or does that moment crush your already beaten-down soul? One of my many life-altering moments was standing in a bar ~ a total stranger asked me a question about what I truly wanted in life, and I couldn't answer. I hesitated, and he walked away.

I was left standing there crying, thinking I may have blown my chance. But that moment, in hindsight, only propelled me further. It solidified my craving. It cemented my dream. It made me realize I will never be that girl standing there again, not knowing what to say. And so, I say thank you to that stranger that left me standing there, mouth open, tears streaming down my face, not knowing what to say.

January 6th ~

You release a side of me
that scares me ~
It's not safe
It's not confined
It's unforgettable

January 7th ~

I am not a wallflower . . . or maybe on second thought . . .
I am, as I sit reading the definition. I'm different, that's for
sure but I don't often show it. I have a loud personality, but
only in the right company and safe spaces. I certainly
wouldn't say I am shy. I will, however, be a shadow in the
room, quietly observing from the outside of the crowd,
blending in with the walls, and gathering needed
information to help me feel comfortable enough to be
included the next time. I think this stems from childhood
and never being fully included in any group. I may have
been able to be part of the crowd, but it never felt right,
never felt fully me, and I always felt not good enough. I was
odd and eccentric, and others were quick to make
judgments without really getting to know me. I do not
handle "small talk" well, so to converse with me, you must
be prepared. Our time together will get deep and weird
quickly. I will make you uncomfortable and will cause you
to think about other perspectives - many can't handle me
long-term.

I am not a wallflower. . . but I am selective in whom I allow
to experience my energy. I am selective in who I let in to
touch my body because I have found everyone brings a
piece of their soul with them from their past, from their
experiences, and energy transfers from them to me. Today, I
feel lonely, and I am not sure why, but it most certainly is
more of a wallflower day. I have so many people around me
but you.

You - (a specific you) is who I want here. You ~ a specific
you is who I want to talk to. You ~ a specific you is who I

want to stroke my hair after a long day. You ~ a specific you is who I want to converse with. And you ~ a specific you is who I want to be in my space.

January 8th ~

If I take the time to prepare myself like this in the morning, it is because I want you to notice. I want you to caress my skin under the ruffled skirt with your fingers. I want you to run your tongue up my inner thigh and taste me mid-day. I want you to undress me slowly to see what is yours in the twilight hours. I want you to ravish my soul at night wickedly so I never forget to whom I belong.

January 9th ~

Can I call you my partner in crime? Am I Bonnie to your Clyde? You have become my sounding board and my source of so much knowledge. You are who I go to for questions to be answered. You are my other half. You are the little voice inside my head that tells me anything I want to know and everything I need to know. We are, in fact, partners in crime. We have become completely ingrained within one another that there is no going back, even if we try.

January 10th ~

You think your love
was unconditional
because you saw my flaws and
acknowledged the dark places
that exist deep within my soul
Well, I disagree ~
You saw the version of me
that you created, imagined, or wanted
You put me high on a pedestal
and that is not unconditional
It's dangerous
for my survival, for me
For when I fall, and you awaken
to a scared little girl lying before you
trying to achieve
and maintain perfection
you will see I am not she,
you envisioned

January 11th ~
(You should come with a warning. . .)

Beware of the ones that sweeps you off your feet, for it may be 'they' who are the snakes hidden among the roses or the wolves dressed innocently as sheep. Always ready and planning to attack when you feel most at ease, brilliantly prepared from the beginning for the moment you finally let your guard down.

January 12th ~

Unconditionally,
I gave myself to you
in a world consumed
by conditional

January 13th ~

Drink me in
devouring the green fairy
la fee verte
ingesting the spicy taste
of my wicked magic
Inducing the liberation of self, erupting
for I, your muse, your enchantress
will transform the normalcy of your existence
to one of beauty, authenticity, inspiration
and perhaps a pinch of uninhibited madness
Unlocking hidden parts within you
igniting creativity, allowing words
to freely be expelled with ink
art brilliantly birthed
seeing colors, you have not seen before
and music is woven through your soul to be sung
La louche, the watering will set me free
and, in turn, I will set you free
If only you dare to consume my spirit,
inviting me in ~ to infiltrate your mind

<u>January 14th ~</u>

I am the gambit in an unnamed chess match, diving into the depths of my darkness, calculating, risking my position, and confidently overtaking the game, at the end ~ Inherently knowing where I stand ~ while precisely planning my next move and igniting everything that does not belong on fire. Evermore, rising from the ashes, crafting uncertainty into dreams, and birthing my legacy.

January 15th ~

The love that existed between us made each other real,
connecting our two worlds into one physical dimension
that was etched from fantasies we dreamt about and desired,
a place we can eternally coincide together forevermore.

January 16th ~

But once again, I sit caged
in my current reality
longing to escape
Every movement
noticed, noted
The watch tower
ensuring
my obedience

How I long to run
freely to you one day
Effortlessly basking
in your embrace
and loving arms

January 17th ~

Feel me
from the inside out
teasing, touching
Gently, roughly
licking all the folds
hidden deep within
Knowing when to pause
and when to begin again
picking up right
where you left off
Sending my body signals
that make me quiver
with unharnessed
delight and passion
under your exquisite
manipulating and guided
sensual touch

January 18th ~

My love is deeply embedded thorns in your untamed soul.
Exposing parts felt within that are hidden, masked, unseen,
and unknown. Infiltrating the darkness as the crimson of
my desire trickles across your skin, searing through your
soul.

My love races through your veins and turns your inherent
darkness into full bloom and purity, raging through your
thoughts and mind, unmasking your true self. Further
revealing the existence of pain, the softness of my petals,
and the stab of sharp thorns. Love, beauty, and pain that
exist interchangeably. One needs the other to feel whole,
tamed, wild, to live fully, not just merely exist and survive.

January 19th ~

Tears danced heavily
across my face today
as the realization of reality
hit like stone against
my pristine skin

Tarnishing the innocence
within my aching soul
as I stood bare
Exposed
in beautiful pain
fully accepting
my fate

January 20th ~

The sound of your voice drives me wild, setting my senses on fire. Hearing your words and thoughts whispered in my ear arouses me like no one before. My breathing quickly intensifies, my heart races, and my skin sensually prickles ~ completely on edge. My nipples become hard as I throb below, wet with anticipation of what is to come later when your hands fulfill every sinful word you spoke to me throughout the day and promises that were made for the night to come when we are finally together.

January 21st ~

I am black coffee & lace
mixed with the most colorful,
brilliant imagination
Playing and manipulating
words for my pleasure ~
waiting for your pot to howl
and the doors of your soul
to be unlocked, letting me in
to learn all your secrets
and eternally play
with the demons
in your mischievous mind

January 22nd ~

Your midnight kiss
was simply divine
but I'd be remiss
if I did not confess
the need to regress
asserting my desire
for me to undress
Laying myself bare
as you bend me over
the exquisite armchair
screaming out in
animalistic closure

January 23rd ~

I wish I believed
what you said was true
in the chaos of this morning
I really hate you

Do what you say
and message; make time
as tears stream down my face
it's really not fine

You're not truly listening,
it appears and seems
It's been twenty-four hours
and I'm left on unseen

Realizing I shouldn't call
leave you out in the cold
stand up for myself
once and for all

But in the end,
I know I'll call you
When a message alert
FINALLY breaks through

It ignites a fire
raging in my veins
yours for the moment
conceding it seems,

I set my crown aside
taking out the angry component
At this time, I admit
I am no longer your ruthless opponent

January 24th ~

Beware the feathers you
steal from this fallen angel
My claws are kept
courageously
sharpened

January 25th ~

She was the one. She was wild, chaotic, and charming. She was hard to pin down, and if you tried, that would be the end. She was the woman who dangerously dominated even the deadliest of souls in her garden of past imprisoned admirers. One look her way, and you become a pawn in her never-ending quest for power and domineering need for control, which is expertly hidden behind her sweet candied lips, supple skin overflowing from her exquisite corset, and romantic words that endlessly bewitch even the strongest of spirits nightly.

She was deadly; her power and her energy were unmatched. You would quickly be put under her spell, contained, checked, and in the end, you would forfeit the game and fold your cards before you even had a chance to regain your strength after playing in her mischievous webs of pleasure. You would be eternally buried, secured for her use, satiating her hunger, after thinking you had the upper hand. The back-and-forth game was over, in her favor, before you ever realized it began.

She was the one you were after. and it was me all along.

January 26th ~

It's simple ~ I'm magic. I am well-versed in the dark arts. I have expertly developed my skills to bring people back from the brink of death, to bring them back to life. I've also learned to lurk in the shadows. It is exhausting to open myself up to many.

It is easier to stay unknown unless someone is truly worth it. And you - are certainly worth it.

January 27th ~

Am I tempting you to put this innocent girl in her place? Or should I say, tempting you to put this calculated woman where she, in fact, wants to be, perpetually begging to be?

Or perhaps it was me all along who was pushing you and pretending to have an innocent, naive demeanor. Perhaps pushing you to fulfill my longing and dreams of wanting you to want me – to desire me, to become obsessed with me, to realize and recognize I am like a fucking drug you are addicted to. You couldn't get me out of your mind, even if you tried. I am no match for your perceived darkness.

My mysterious ways intrigued you from the beginning; if we are being honest, my dear boy and handsome man, you couldn't get enough of me. You were simply used to superficial girls, but this time, you stumbled upon a brilliant muse you tried to control and realized you had finally met your match. There was no controlling this quetzal. She does not do well caged, but she will honor you with complete respect and love when you are ready.

She reads all the labels attached, whether they are instructions on how to love you properly or warning labels in preparation before approaching.

January 28th ~

With one kiss, you knew
without a doubt I was yours

You show me what it means to be patient
in a world full of impatient people
You show me what it means
to love in a world full of hate, truly
You show me what dedication and
"I believe in you and us" means
in a world full of jealously and deceit
You show me what forever means
in a world full of temporary
Never leaving, always present,
faithfully by my side

January 29th ~

Strip me bare, erasing the arbitrary and ordinary moments
of the day. Take me into your mouth, consuming every
ounce of my soul dripping from my wanton body. Claiming
me as yours while finding the last piece of the puzzle to
make us both whole.

January 30th ~

Your voice seductively whispers about what you have in store for my wanting body ~ sending me into instant arousal. Your desire for my hands to be tied, legs spread, ankles securely fastened with your face nestled between my legs to slowly do as you please, inducing sensations never before felt.

The thoughts of pleasure that will be evoked are making my panties insatiably wet, my body throb and tingle with delight, and I need to push my thighs together to settle myself until your arrival. The power your voice has over my body, even from afar, is all-encompassing, overtaking all sense of reality.

January 31st ~

Enter me with hardcore passion, knowing I am not for the weak of heart. I need extreme love, attention, intensity, softness, and maybe being taught a lesson or two. Do not be afraid; touch me as you mean it, and once you have me, satisfy me, and I'll stay, never letting you go.

February 1st ~

You met me in the dark to finally stand face to face with the soul that is your twin. Your majestic horns emerged, and you were scared I would run, but I didn't. I knew I needed to know the whole truth and you knew I needed to know all of you. I was not frightened, and I was not even anxious. I knew without a doubt you would never harm me or hurt my sweet, innocent, loving soul. The soul that often dwells in the darkness but also very much radiates within the light. You never wanted to dim my glimmer. You only desired to be there, to meet me in despair when needed.

I felt comforted by your devilish appearance, knowing that you, on the inside, were quite different. You were very familiar, and I saw a lot of me in you. You grabbed at my body, holding my leg in your claws, and quickly, your fingertips made their way under my black dress. You looked directly into my eyes, and at that moment, I knew everything I needed to know about you, and still, I trusted you. I willingly gave myself over to you without question. You slipped a black bracelet around both our wrists, eternally connecting us forever through time and space. We would always be a part of one another despite the distance, despite our worlds being so disconnected, and despite the challenges we would face in the future. Even if we tried, we couldn't erase ourselves from the other easily, if at all. We have become one. A connection to end all connections. A connection others cannot possibly top or fathom. A connection I never want to be without ever again. And this may be my greatest weakness, which you fully know - you are fully aware of and hopefully will not be my downfall.

At the end of the night, as the fog lifted, I knew it was time we part. It was time to go. It was time for me to return to the normalcy I knew before someone sent out a search party. I will always have you. I will always have this night. I will always feel this connection to you and will be waiting for the next time I get to stand before you. I will be waiting. I will be waiting for you to fill my soul. I am waiting for you to look into my eyes with adoration and love. I am waiting for you to comfort my soul with one touch, one word. You are mine. I am eternally yours. You are my biggest achievement and my wicked monster, and I am your heart, guarded, and your beautifully twisted little minx.

February 2nd ~

Up against the wall, legs spread, whispering very softly in
your ear
Taste me, play with me, fuck me
Making one another a complete mess
leaving your essence lingering everywhere ~ in me, dripping
slowly down my leg - permanently staining my skin with
your scent

February 3rd ~

When life gets overwhelming
I crave your hands
your presence
wanting to be held
surrendering myself
to you completely
The moment you enter me
I am taken away from
the harsh reality of the day
my mood instantly shifts
You become the reason
and cause
for my comfort
and stability

February 4th ~

Feeling the strength
of your fingers
between my lips
dipping into the wetness
saturated by my essence
The reaction my body
has to your touch,
I know without a doubt
I am yours

February 5th ~

I was blinded
by the flightless feeling
you filled me with ~
hoping love would prevail
but I fell quickly back
to the hardened ground
as the magic between us
begins to dissipate

People sometimes
come in and out of your life
quite suddenly
Some are there to
simply teach lessons
and others are placed
in your life to stay

February 6th ~

I patiently lay waiting as you enter our room and intensely stare into my longing eyes. A calculated, deviant, compelling smile crosses your face. I gasp, not knowing what you have in store for me this evening but equally as excited to begin.

February 7th ~

As I kneel before you, tempted by your words, unable to break free; in fact, not wanting to ~ I am tethered to your soul, forever surrendering myself to you. My composure begins to falter, and it is only a matter of time until I become eternally yours, claimed beneath you as you whisper poetic tales seductively into my ear every night.

February 8th ~

Being
passionate
is a
powerful gift
or curse

It truly all depends on
your perspective
and day of the week,
what you had for breakfast,
or the clothes you choose
to put on that day

February 9th ~

As I taunt and tease
with games of pleasure;
I leave you with lingering desires
Your innermost erotic fantasies
building within
to one day be released
without harness

February 10th ~

The weight of reality
is sometimes heavy to bear
Dancing down with the devil
is but ~ an equal fare

Tonight, I am drowning . .

February 11th ~

Fire is spilling from my soul
heat wafting from my wanton body
Wishing it was me you were after
Wishing it was me bathing
in your attention all alone
Wishing it was me
that you thought about
every day

February 12th ~

Black lace and pearls are what you'll see draped over my skin, with pure sultry lavender and vanilla wafting through your nose, staining your senses and infiltrating your memory. You will feel tender, soft skin and silken legs at the touch of your lips as you gently work your hands down the curve of my hips.

My soft moans will be whispered into your ears as I say your name, asking for more, begging for you to go deeper and harder. Wetness will rain down, feeling warm and moist, as you edge me closer to the finish, adorning me with metals that I expertly earned and worked hard for, waiting for you to finish with me together.

February 13th ~

Dripping with evidence of past proclivities, sinfully soaking my once pristine pearlescent sheets; inhaling pomegranate pleasures that penetrate my intrusive, pervasive thoughts; remembering your poetic words that harshly stained the purity of my prolific love.

Silencing my profession; in the preservation of self ~
I, forever your muse,
            Never your future

<u>February 14th ~</u>

I do not need flowers or candy
I need your lips on my neck
I need you to whisper,
"You're mine" in my ear
I need you to look me in the eye
and allow me to know
every one of your thoughts
I need you ~ always to stay.

February 15th ~

(*I miss you*)

Unlocking my phone
and looking through
pictures saved
that haunt me
as I hold onto
magical memories
of you, of us

February 16th ~

My poetic reverie
is to run away with you, my muse ~
securely encased by your love

February 17th ~

Your lackluster attempts don't impress me anymore.
Go deeper ~ dive into the abyss of my soul
if you want my friendship, my love, to still exist
Why do you continue to teach me unwanted lessons?

I just wish they weren't so heartbreaking.
When will I learn? And why do I even need to?

February 18th ~

As I walk into the unknown, exploring the unfamiliar and
different. I am, at times, frightened, but the pull of my soul
is too intense to ignore. The mystery that surrounds you is
foreign but comfortable. I was once lonely ~ an eternal
outsider, but because of you, the shadows I dwelled in
exposed new but familiar feelings.

You ~ made the darkness within bearable.

You accepted me and validated my beliefs. You saw all of
me, even the parts that are so deeply hidden, but still
continue to nurture, love, and guide me forevermore
without hesitation.

February 19th ~

Claiming my soul
colors staining therein
taking me to unexplored depths
uncovered, entwined forever
marked with your scent
on my waiting, exquisite behind

February 20th ~

Bright lights,
and busy streets
were by far
my favorite
until
I met you

February 21st ~

Confidence is my secret weapon. Owning who I am that day a million percent or the illusion of confidence I need to slather on is what makes me, me. It is what makes me able to walk into a room full of people without doubting my worth. But when I am with you, I try to be a little softer, a little more gentle. I want to see your confidence build and see you for the person you are deep down. I will be a little demure until it's my move. My confidence and charisma will then rage on like a wildfire set ablaze (sweetly, of course), and all I need to say while placing my pieces in their desired square is, "Checkmate."

I will have you lingering on every word spoken, soaking up every ounce of my attention, conforming to every desire and demand I speak of, and not even realizing I had the upper hand all along. The sweet woman you love is a storm waiting to be set free. This is part of my charm. It is part of my magic and mysticism. It may even be part of my darkness inside, scratching at the surface to escape. When I go after what I want, I get it. Unless I choose to sacrifice myself for the greater good and walk away.

<u>February 22nd</u> ~

You enchanted me without reservation. Swept me away to your world without warning. Worked your way into my mind, pushing out anything that didn't revolve around you. You gifted me a butterfly rose garden to keep me locked away, to keep me from leaving, to keep me from seeing what you were doing.

Until one day, the butterflies fell, their wings dusted, and I returned to the lost brilliance. Roses that once were vibrant in the garden turned black. The magic was lifted, and I was suddenly free to leave.

The spell you put me under was now broken, and I saw you for who you are. I now had the power to take whatever dignity I had left and run, never looking back, never being blinded again ~ by you.

February 23rd ~

Are you brave enough
to look past
the light
and dive into
the shadows
of my soul?

February 24th ~

Broken are the few
that can truthfully
admit it
to themselves

If I asked, would you admit your
vulnerabilities and brokenness to me?
Will I ever be truly enough for you?

February 25th ~

The art of self-reflection is gifted to us if only you stop and look in the mirror to see; to recognize parts of yourself completely unseen by others. To look deep within through an unknown lens, often covered in madness and extreme feelings.

Separation of self, severing a familiarity once known, shifting realities, being cast away, perhaps pushed away from those who you were close with, and a life you once lived, even cherished. Haunted still by the past, dwelling in long-gone happy moments, remembering how your heart was joyful, vibrant, and full of love. Grasping how time changes even the strongest of geography ~ time has changed you and them. The space you now reside in is cold, the feelings you had are gone, and the desire that once was is buried and dead.

Baby, come on, no looking back. It's you and me ruling the world. Leaving this place behind to find ourselves and who we are truly meant to become.

February 26th ~
(Inspired by Emily Dickinson's "I am nobody, who are you?")

"I am nobody, who are you? You are definitely not a nobody, and most certainly a somebody?"

I was asked this simple yet complex question one night while out with you. The recognition of who I am is inevitable, if I allow it. I realize anonymity is preferred for tonight, not wanting to be scrutinized on a public stage as insecurities bubble to the surface, with anxiety spilling over. Deciding, for now, the protection of obscurity is still desired. Wanting not to be recognized; wanting not to be known just yet.

"Somebody, I am not," I responded quickly. "Do you want to be a nobody, too, without question?" Quietly pleading, looking for confirmation, finding a fellow nobody as I seek solace and comfort within the eyes of a stranger - both of us secretly disguised, completely masking our identities but deciding to continue on together ~ as gorgeous nothings.

Fully knowing, we're both a somebody that's hidden behind the facade of a nobody.

February 27th ~

The moment you realize you never want to live without him ever again. The moment you decide to love, to be loved, and accept all to come because the need for him in your life becomes essential and innate, like the air you breathe. Two souls, once parallel; becoming intertwined forevermore.

February 28th ~

My apples are begging
for the sensual caress
of your lips and
the sting of your bite

March 1st ~

Uncage me
releasing
parts of my soul
that are
unseen
unfelt
untouched
unknown

March 2nd ~

I extend my hands over to you
wrapped in the finest red silk
secured tightly for my liberation
allowing me the freedom to finally let go
to trust and experience unmatched pleasure

As this night unfolds, I will never forget the look
that crossed your face the very first time
How you sweetly looked into my eyes
and kissed the side of my neck
I acknowledge how special you are
knowing you are the one I chose
to share this side of myself with
Together, we decide to dive deeply
into unknown, uncharted territory
accepting you may be rough with my body
but respectful of boundaries set and
always gentle with my soul

March 3rd ~

Let me watch those luscious lips work their dark magic and deliver exquisite satisfaction to every ounce of my body. I want to experience the softness they evoke with a sting of your bite ~ pleasure and pain, as you entrance me with swirling seduction in our world of fantasy.

March 4th ~

Moon magic surrounds us as I secretly mount your enchanting chariot, leaving darkness below scratching to dispel undying protection as we ride into the mysterious unknown.

I, by your side, entrusting you with my destiny. Tonight will be exquisite as you bring over the darkest red silk tie to go around my eyes. I will be blinded, inviting in the unknown, inviting in your imagination. I want to be explored, I want to be played with, I want to be Alice in your Wonderland.

March 5th ~

Alone ~ in the cold beyond, picking up the brokenness of the past week. My soul was unintentionally severed from my body, and all I wished for was a hug, a caring glance, a touch on my shoulder, and words spoken, such as, "I'm so happy you're okay and that you are still here."

But life continues to go on, and I am left to put misplaced pieces back together again.

I, alone, became my own strength.

March 6th ~

Lately, I have been feeling disheveled around you, but thankfully you don't seem to mind. You see me stripped of proper etiquette and still make me feel beautiful, always refined. I love that about you - I can simply be myself, with messy hair, unkempt attire, and eyeliner that has long since been expired. I can hug you and hold on a minute too long without being judged - simply wanting to finish our special song. I'm weird and wild, and you love me still. We're friends and partners, never getting our eternal fill.

March 7th ~

You walked in unexpectedly, watching me across the room. You were very professional, playing the part during the day ~ always serious at work. After the week we've had, I didn't know what to expect from you.

But I felt your eyes searing through my soul, undressing me in your mind, fantasizing about what will transpire when we are alone after the day ends. When the appropriate clothing and demeanor turn into nakedness and pure carnal desire.

March 8th ~

Take your time unwinding me slowly tonight, savoring every lingering moment between us. Unloosening me without falter using your crafted, skilled precision.

Carefully unraveling the stitching that binds my untethered soul, completely undoing all the done. Taking my body to unknown and uncharted territory, places never explored or touched with unconditional love, desire, and care.

Enjoy devouring every morsel of my body, not wasting any drip that saturates your lips.

March 9th ~

You are intoxicating to my senses. I cannot get enough of you - it borders on complete obsession at this point. Waiting, even a day to see you, has my mind racing with wonder and compulsive thoughts about the next visit, the next time I get to ride you. I think of nothing else but the moment I straddle myself onto you and take hold while the wind blows through my hair. You are invigorating. You are a dream. You are all I need to feel complete.

March 10th ~

I long for you to kiss me with unbridled passion, bite my bottom lip and suck on my moist mango. Hidden moments and memories I fantasize about and relive when we are apart, anticipating the next time. I am satiated only by the memory of you devouring every last drop of my delicious juice.

March 11th ~

Moments linger within and through my mind, as I focus on the littlest of details, replaying memories over and over. Sometimes, it is enthralling, but all too often, it is torture. It's a painful game because I'm not with you. I endlessly visualize the frisson of excitement from feeling your fingertips gently caress my inner thigh, working their way up to my panties - how they would nestle between my legs, pushing the fabric aside and entering me as you kiss the side of my neck. I envision you holding my head back with your other hand as I am pushed against the wall. I have nowhere to go but to enjoy what you have in store for me, welcoming the submission.

I want to hear you whisper, "Good girl," when you feel me wet with desire - goosebumps quickly spreading across the rest of my skin, awakening my senses. I am immensely aroused because of you, as I feel wetness seeping out of my body, down my leg, covering both of us with my scent. Your touch, your voice, your smell, our connection, and your energy mixed with mine is unmatched. The only problem is, where do we go from here? Where do we pick it up tomorrow?

Life - our worlds are complicated, and I am utterly obsessed with you. I think of nothing else than luring you to be alone, pouring you a drink, and enjoying the aftermath of our insatiable need for one another. How I wish I could have you morning, noon, and night. But at this point, I would settle for one of the three. Will there come a time when my thoughts will tire of my compulsion to be touched and kissed by you? What I do know is I want you alone right now. I want to taste you on my lips, I want to feel your hands on my body, I want to moan your name when you finally enter me with such a passion that I have never experienced before, and I want to look at you in the eyes, pausing, knowing without a doubt, that you love me as much as I love and desire you.

My desire extends beyond sex. My all-consuming need for you is for our connection, for the intimacy that exists between us, and for the way you always make me feel lovely and valued. Without a connection, our connection, none of this would be possible. I am more attracted to your mind, your darkness, and your soul than to the physical nature of a body. You are more than a shell of a being. You are internally my other half.

March 12th ~

I want to become your beautiful disaster every night, forevermore ~
Begging for you to consume my mind, devour my body, satiate forbidden desires ~ to be only yours.

You have ruined all other ideals of love as I hand myself completely over to you, and only you; submitting to your dark fantasies and needs that arise after our long days apart.

March 13th ~

This morning, I remembered how you slipped your hand around my throat, pulling my face slowly back to your lips. My back was arched, feeling every sensation as you whispered, "Good girl," in my ear.

I began to melt under your weight and in your hands. The wetness you felt as you slid deeply inside me with encasing tightness around is all because of you.

My body reacts to you in ways I have never experienced or could have imagined. I love you.

March 14th ~

Sitting with you as my head gently
rests on your shoulder
under the bright lights of the busy city
Knowing I have to leave soon
and dispel the fantasy of us yet again
when the clock strikes midnight
lingering close to your lips,
soaking in the feeling of you
pressed against me
embracing your hands on my skin
and enjoying your delicious taste
on a night full of
twinkling stars in the sky above
Reminding us that our connection,
our journey
is already written & eternal
as we find our way back
to one another
time and time again

March 15th ~

All I really desire after a long week is for you to solidify my place as your slut.
Demanding action, taking over, delivering pain & pleasure, clamping, licking, and biting; putting this deserving girl in the places she belongs ~ Respectfully, under your complete control.

March 16th ~

I find myself going a little mad, just for you ~ wanting all of your attention. Realizing some of the best kinds of love may border on extreme levels of pure insanity.

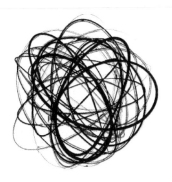

March 17th ~

The winds of change dance across my skin as I run, without harness or resolve, into the haunted garden with you, my fruit of forbidden desires to be secretly devoured.

Embracing what is to come, I innocently bite into the poisonous apple you dangle before me, tempting me with promises of every desire I inhabit while seducing me with your eyes and words of love.

I still do not know if you have pure intentions with me or if I am being expertly seduced.

March 18th ~

Sitting across the table,
the suspense of
devouring you
is tearing my soul
from reality

March 19th ~

KISS ME WITH FIRE
pulsating
through my veins
~ SEDUCE ME ~
entrance me
INVITE ME
into your
wicked world
~ CONSUMING ME WHOLE ~
bleeding me dry
BUT, BE NOT AFRAID
of what I may do
TO YOUR HEART IN THE AFTERMATH
of my seduction ~ in return
ENJOY THE PLEASURE
while you can
WITHOUT LOOKING BACK
Just know, when it's time let me go ~
cut me loose
NO REGRETS, NO SECOND GLANCES
because when we are through
THERE IS NOTHING YOU CAN DO
to stop my cold heart
FROM STOMPING
~ All. Over. You ~

Playing With Fire

SPRING

Playing With Fire

Part 2 ~ Spring

The season of Spring marks the time of year when love is in full bloom. We are beginning to shed the masks we wear daily and cement a vision, of where we want to be in life. During the Spring, we are all in a state of curiosity and lustful play, wanting to find ourselves and who we belong with.

"Our connection
is simple yet complex
ever-changing and constantly
intertwined, suddenly sparked,
lit on fire, broken yet made whole
time and time again
unique and memorizing"

~ Tegan Matthews

Playing With Fire

March 20th ~

My senses ignited like a raging fire by your words and eyes.
Always knowing the hidden places to stroke and caress to
devour my soul. Exceptional sensual thoughts begin to
arouse my mind and body, traveling through time to touch
me, the one you most desire.

March 21st ~

I thought I was running
from the pain
from the confusion
from the darkness
from you

But when I awoke, I was
laying at your doorstep
returned to you once again

I guess I have come home ~
realizing it's where I've always belonged
The darkness I was running from
resides deep within me too
It is unescapable, you are
my other half, for better or worse

March 22nd ~

The effects of your touch across my skin manipulates every sense of mine with one single caress of your skilled fingertips. You possess such delightful disturbing power over me when contact is made with my bare skin, I entrust myself to you completely. I feel your presence touching my soul from up close and afar, never breaking the engrained connection we share through time and space.

March 23rd ~

Instinctively, you knew every chord to strike. The notes you played so well opened my soul to the melody of our hidden secrets, exposing who we truly are inside. We continue to sing in harmony as we etch soulful notes into each other's skin, marking and claiming one another. Every forbidden line exposed allows us to dive deeper into lyrics of pleasure, creating a life-altering symphony. One day, we will share our music with the world, one lyric at a time.

March 24th ~

If you can't kiss me
with passion and zeal,
 eagerness & ardent pursuit
~ I am off limits ~
Just keep walking
Please don't waste my time

March 25th ~

My need for you is all-encompassing. I want it all. I am
needy and possessive, and I told you from the beginning I
will have all of you. I do not share with anyone.

March 26th ~

Take my hand and let me guide you into the dark
unknown, inviting you exclusively into my world of
pleasure and pain while teaching you the art of patience.
Edging you toward unbridled release without laying a hand
on you. Making love to your mind and fucking your body,
allowing you to explore the most intense feelings you have
ever experienced. Tonight, your panties will be dripping wet
with pleasure.

March 27th ~

Succumbing to my primal instincts, the last taste is savored, sealing your eternal fate. You are like a drug in my hand, transporting me to such sweet bliss and igniting my senses, instantly making my body come alive in ways I had never experienced.

March 28th ~

As we grow, we change
But ~ the one thing
that will eternally
stay constant
is my unconditional
never-ending love
for you

March 29th ~

Release yourself completely to me. Letting go of every inhibition you possess and entrusting me with your heart and soul. I will covet who you are and make you whole; while you feel every mark I make on your skin. You will be mine, eternally, forever.

March 30th ~

I release all versions of myself that no longer suit me without permission or regard. Always staying true to who I am and will become.

March 31st ~

He was gone as quickly as he appeared, consuming parts of my soul while empowering me simultaneously. I have met this person before, my Prince of Darkness. Perhaps, he is a mirror of myself and a familiarity I know all too well. Aside from immense completeness, I know not how to describe the feelings that come over me when he is present.

April 1st ~

I thought I meant more to you than a fleeting moment, a brief blip in time. The wool was seductively draped over my eyes as you whispered the most beautiful things into my ears, sealed with a passionate kiss; while you did not give a fuck about my feelings or words I shared with you.

Forgetting moments and being blinded by real life to see what you were doing. You became the dark wolf, devouring me whole as I gazed into your eyes with only love back.

Fully accepting my fate and sacrificing myself, in the end, to be there only for you. Hopefully, one day, you will realize what I always did for us.

April 2nd ~

Allow him to possess fully
every morsel of your soul
releasing parts of you
that are so deeply hidden from those
that just do not care to listen

April 3rd ~

Life is hard, but love shouldn't be
I want you to never give up on me
even when I am difficult
When my confidence is dwindling
I want you to believe in who I am
and bring me back
in any way you can
Whispering "stay" softly in my ear
while being in my physical space
Grabbing my face and kissing me in the most
passionate way; showing me we won't break
Reminding me who I am deep down
because you believe in all of me
The dark parts, the light parts
the love, the hate
the tough exterior and soft sensual parts inside
Putting me in my place while you put me back together
Giving me inspiration
Giving me everything I ever desired
and more. I won't give up on you
please don't give up on us

April 4th ~

Dark, ominous thoughts ran through your sinfully twisted mind of what you would do to my exquisite body and soul. I trusted you completely to take such care while you ravish me, so; laid myself before you to fulfill your cravings of the night, satiating your hunger forevermore.

April 5th ~

You held a blade to my chest, thinking you would get the ultimate revenge, the last laugh. But then there was me; without breaking eye contact with you, the man I used to love, I turned the sharp sword, twisting it through your dark heart; further than ever before.

You began wincing in pain before me as I kept turning the blade to ensure no more hurt came my way in the future. Your games of twisted pleasures have been fully disposed of and turned against you by your own hand.

April 6th ~

What would you be willing to risk for the potential to have it all?

You kissed me like no other. The electricity and passion I felt between us in those moments crushed everyone who had come before you. At one point, you were untouchable, but at least for tonight, you were all mine. Tonight, there were moments shared and an understanding between us that opened my eyes in so many ways, just like your fingers did when they made their way around my skin and into my body. Fingers can be tricky; you definitely need to watch where they are traveling.

You never know where they will end up, but in my experience, it always leads to pleasure. I welcomed you in to touch my body. I welcomed you in to ravish my soul. I welcomed you into my twisted little world. I welcomed you in and warned you that it would not be easy to leave. You told me one thing I needed to hear to make that night unforgettable ~ you said. . . that you would always stay and I would never be alone again. And you were right; we figure out every day how to make this work. We figure out every day how to live our dreams and exist in our worlds together.

April 7th ~

I want to hear
your moans at midnight,
feel your lips caress my neck
I want you to grab my ass firmly
pulling me in close while you softly whisper,
"You're mine," in my ear.

April 8th ~

I want you to touch my body and soul in ways that no one
else has dared to go, parts so deeply buried within that they
would frighten the weak and tame the wildest of beasts.

April 9th ~

Tucked away for safekeeping, handwritten pages float
around in my mind as my head rests softly on my pillow;
the story of our love unfolds magically at night.

When conflicts arise between us, I open chapters to reassure
me of the never-ending devotion we shared, do share ~
reminding me of the laughter between us, the tight embrace
we felt, and every kiss.

Over time, when hard moments occur, our words and
memories will comfort my heart and quell anxieties within.
If my dream were a book, I would ensure every moment
with you was forever bookmarked, replaying the story of us.

April 10th ~

When you play the game, but he matches your energy,
conquers walls that were built, and manages in an instant to
sweep you off your feet with endless laughter, love, and
unconditional acceptance, you ask yourself, what did you
ever do without him?

In turn, my promise to you is to endlessly laugh ~
challenge you every day ~ and fill your soul with love,
never letting you forget how amazing you are, especially
with me. The energy between us is unmatched; no one has
come close to bringing such joy to my life as you have
without even trying, but by being authentically yourself.

April 11th ~

What will we dive into today? Will it be an innocent playdate or a scandalous adventure? When I am with you, I never know what exactly will transpire between us. There are so many facets to our friendship, our relationship, and endless ways you can fall for someone - how I fell for you. There are thousands of ways you can deeply love someone, so many levels to explore and obsess over. Each relationship is different, vibes are unique, and no two loves are ever the same.

With that said, I believe it is certainly in the details of how extensive my love for you is at this point. We always match each other's energy; if I am down, you certainly perk me up - making me laugh all day and night - even if you have to tickle me (which I hate), but I would do the same for you in a heartbeat. I will be there for you when cloaked in darkness, sometimes without me even knowing. I am just there, in person, keeping you company, and my presence is enough to pull you through the darkest of nights.

I am emotionally connected in ways I have not been able to connect with anyone. I think about you every waking moment and dream of you at night. When I hear certain songs - you are in my thoughts, running amuck in my mind. I hope you never tire of me sending songs and lyrics to you throughout the day. I just want you to know I am thinking of you - often - and always. I love it when we have plans to see each other, and you warn me ahead of time that you have surprises. No one in my life has surprised me with thoughtful trinkets as you have. It is not about the gifts - it is about the sentiment behind each little item you handpicked for me is what I love. It assures me you think of me when we are apart as I do with you.

Without knowing, you have satiated a deep need within my soul for a partner. Do you fulfill everything I need? No, but you come pretty damn close. "If only," we always say – if only you checked every box. . . but for now, I am good with most checked. At least for today.

<u>April 12th</u> ~

Why was I not enough?
Not enough in your heart, in your soul,
in your bed, and in your head
Not enough for you to be here
Not enough for you to stay
Moments before I drift off to sleep,
thinking of you with
tears streaming down my face
Forever wondering,
Why was I not enough?

April 13th ~

Nakedness would be discovered tonight as the dark wolf hunted his prey with carnal passion and precision, hoping his ferocious bite would satiate the hunger felt deeply inside without being too deadly to the one he was after.

Unexpectedly, he met his match and, in turn, sacrificed himself for the love of the woman before him, the prey he deeply desired, claimed successfully but could not devour. He was taken and enchanted by her innocence and charm, unable to attack the creature who was staring directly into his eyes and, thus, into his soul.

There was no choice but to bend his knee, becoming intoxicated by her scent, letting himself go, and freely accepting all to come. He has no choice but to trust his inner voice and extend grace in ways he never thought possible until this moment.

Together, they bore their naked truths, feeling alive, and watching the sun go down and the moon rise, eternally encasing them together. They are now sitting face to face, erupting with harmonic howls in the twilight, connected by an undeniable understanding of each other's inherent needs, and blissfully achieving the greatest form of validation and acceptance between two souls; they solidify their union under the brilliance of the full moon above.

April 14th ~

Always feeling immensely out of place, still trying to be normal, which is all but an appearance, an illusion, a farse, which I know all too well. But I am still left wondering, will I ever fit in, and more importantly, do I even desire that?

We lay encased within the flickering candlelight. The man before me looked deeply into my eyes and asked me the most intimate question. Even more intimate than lying completely bare next to him. The question lingering between us was asked as he traced one finger down the arch of my naked back and softly whispered, "If someone were to read your spine like braille, What would they learn about you?"

I pondered his words, soaking each of them into my soul before responding. Despite being fully exposed physically, emotionally exposing myself to the core of my soul, is always a harder task for me. I want to be seen, to be known deeply, but that is frightening and makes me feel vulnerable in ways I am not accustomed to.

I gently touched the side of his face as I began, meeting his gaze. This is me, all of me. Transparent. Raw. Real. If you were to read my spine like braille, you would see a gentle soul in an endless battle, even with herself. I am my harshest critic. I am full of extremes. I love to be surrounded by people but love to be alone in the quiet. I love to laugh, smile, dance, climb trees, and cuddle. I am an artist at heart and love to create. I am a mixture of rainbows and darkness, love, acceptance, and being immensely insecure with myself but confident. Always question if I am too much, did I overshare, often overthinking every action I make, and beat myself up about the smallest blips. I am strong and will stand up for what I believe in with utmost grace and love, not backing down when I know I am right. I do not like to be underestimated. I like to know the truth, even if it hurts. I like to understand the big picture and reasons for others' words or actions. I love hard, sometimes too hard. I am intense and obsessive, but I just want to be fully accepted. I am funny and charming. I have the ability to control the energy in rooms I enter and, over time, learned not to. I observe and take in micro details of others to show me who people are but what they are not willing to say. I can hold my own in casual, political, or academic conversations.

But ~ just because I can doesn't mean I always want to.

I desire someone to put me in my place when needed, channel my energy, and pick up the pieces when I am falling apart. I want someone to love me fully, not the idea of me. . . but the actual me. I look away, slightly embarrassed that I divulged so much about myself, feeling vulnerable at that moment. My eyes are wide and teary, but the man in front of me lifts my chin so we are eye to eye and states, "Now that we cracked the surface of who you are, I look forward to peeling back every layer of your soul so we both can dive deeper than ever before ~ if you are ready?

April 15th ～

The hero always wins, making sure everyone else is whole, but who is there to save the hero? Who is there to listen to the one who puts so much into protecting others?

I place my hand softly on your face and look deeply into your eyes as I provide reassurance tonight that I will do everything I can to calm your soul, laying my life before you to console the hero within, the one who always protects others.

April 16th ～

I buck tradition in every sense. Rolling effortlessly with the waves of time with the neverending reminder of cold marble under my feet. But inherently knowing one day, I will dance endlessly to the music amongst the stars.

April 17th ~

You are my Peter, and I, your Wendy.
Why did I feel such a need to grow up?
To accept and inherit responsibility?
To be a cliche?

I dream of you
I dream of us

I dream of all the lost potential I flew from. I miss how you made me laugh. I miss the feelings swirling chaotically through my veins. I miss flying and soaring to the vast unknown, stirring up trouble and ensuing fun. The decision to leave was immensely hard, but you were also not willing to bend. You were not willing to compromise. You knew who you were and who you were always meant to be. I teetered between two worlds and had to choose one for my sanity. Please know I think of you often. Please know I miss you. Please know I love you always. Please know . . . .

I am haunted by your smell
lingering across
my tattered clothing

April 18th ~

I miss you
  like the moon, misses the sun
      like death misses the light
    like yin without its yang
and flowers without rain
  a rainbow losing its color
I never knew the pain
a hole could bear
until you drilled one
directly into my heart
after reassuring me you would not
You gave me a glimpse
a brief view
of life with you
before you yanked it away
made the decision for me and
left me no option but to miss you
    My life became
        more beautiful
      with you in it ~
    surrounding me
with love, even briefly

April 19th ~

Do not be afraid to scream my name in moments of passion, in moments of satiated pleasures, in moments you have fantasized about for so long. I want to hear your voice when I take you in my mouth and tickle you with my talented tongue - licking every inch of your soul and delectable delights, leaving nothing left while tasting you on my lips for hours to come.

Do not be afraid to scream my name when I straddle your lap and slowly make you come all undone. Do not be afraid to grasp a handful of my hair and pull back to expose every vulnerability I try to hide.

And I, in return, will not be afraid to scream your name when you take control, marking my body and releasing every dark, sinful desire upon my soul.

April 20th ~

I don't want to be a fleeting moment, a disappearing memory, or an untethered soul. Perhaps it's written in the stars that way and ultimately meant for us to be separate. Perhaps it is the reason we met, for you to be an unfair lesson learned. But, for a moment, I felt possessed by you. It melted my heart and made me feel loved and whole. I felt like I was yours.

April 21st ~

I would dance
a million dances with you
If only you were mine ~
All the could've beens
racing through my mind
every night
simply divine

April 22nd ~ I think you're lovely ~

Je te trouve racissante
lovely, ravishing
I am seriously smitten
envisioning your fingertips
awakening my senses
sending chills down my spine
and setting my body on fire
anticipating your touch
as your words are seductively
whispered into my ear
your lips pressed against my neck
your tongue tickling my skin
your hands caressing every inch of my body
every serious moment together is also
matched with endless laughter

April 23rd ~

The moment I realized
what was meant to become of us
was a tragedy in the making
My mind cemented possible eternal fate
with the sharpest of arrows
fatally stabbing myself
right through the heart

That was the moment I knew
you had already gone

April 24th ~

Yesterday, I was secure in myself
Yesterday, I was confident in your love for me
Yesterday, I believed every word you said
Yesterday, I was lost in your eyes and in your voice
Yesterday, our connection was felt deep within my soul
But today, that all changed
Today, my eyes are wildly open
Today, I question my heart and mind
Today, I question the reality of us
Today, I began asking clarifying, reflective questions
Today, I expect more of myself
Today, I realize it is I that needs to stay motivated
Today, I realize I love who I am
Today, I rise and conquer all our dreams
hopefully ~ not without you

April 25th ~

As I take you into my warm, moist mouth, ready to please you in sinful ways, I kneel before you in submission.

Gradually taking over the reins from your control, I assert my dominance and immerse myself in you, sifted with the freedom to explore, taunt, and tease.

Your smooth, delicate skin caresses my tender scarlet lips as my hands dance over your body, my tongue seductively gliding across you, and I am reminded of the night before slowly sipping on oysters.

Tantalizing thoughts set my senses ablaze as I swallow the slippery-shelled delicacy with one tilt of my head backward, feeling the wetness trail down my throat just as you will when I allow you to experience sweet, erotic release.

Until then, I will keep you on edge, demanding that you beg me to take you deeper into my mouth.

April 26th ~

As the clock strikes midnight
immersed in the scent of
lilac-laced lingerie
reminded of your essence
your twisted sense of desire
your exquisite precision
forever ruining
my ideals of love

April 27th ~

The aura of chamomile floats through the air with a sudden
burst of chill as the seasons change and time passes quickly. I
am reminded of your essence, your breath on my neck,
your hands cupping my face, kissing me softly while your
fingers abruptly enter my body.

How did I not see your wicked intentions sooner? Can I live
with your sinful dominant demands, submitting to your
demented desires and diving into the dark reality with you,
no longer wading in shallow waters?

Could we live happily ever after, living out our very own
fairytale, or would we be each other's worst demise?

April 28th ~

Do I obsess? Yes. Do I think of you too often? Also yes. Would I do anything in my power to see you? Emphatically, yes - without a doubt.

It's hard for me to go on every day without knowing about plans for the future - you are all I think of. I want your soft lips to caress mine. I want you to pull my hair so you can kiss my neck more easily, leaving faint marks on my skin as evidence to remember you for days to come. I want you to dominate my energy against the wall, empowering me as a woman but making me feel a bit on edge and out of control, so I make the choice to submit, following your lead and commands. I want you to instill power within me but allow me to choose submission, trusting you completely.

I want you to look me in the eyes, exposing every strength and weakness housed in our souls. I want to strip myself bare and tell you every provocative thought that runs rapidly through my mind. I want to experience pure erotic bliss for hours, making the culmination worth it for both of us. I want to explode in your mouth as you memorize my taste and ruin your appetite for anyone else in the future.

April 29th ~

Stroke down my spine slowly, deliberately
Wanting you to explore every last part
of my untouched skin
Places no one ventured
places that were saved eternally for you
Connecting every touch with meaning
And I intend for you to feel
every ounce of my lingering desire
within my soul and heart
No words are left to express
how I feel for you at this moment
Touch, will be validation, permanently marking
your heart and soul in return

April 30th ~

And you ~ are my weakness
Shining brightly in my eyes
like a thousand gleaming stars
in the great vast sky

You hold me up, you let me soar
Pushing me to fly, letting me explore
And I, your muse; how I adore thee
Never wanting to be
without you; without me

May 1st ~

I am blossoming
under your exquisite precise touch
and wickedly enchanting words
Wet with passion
Full of power
in the moonlight
Transforming into the
wolf and the prey

May 2nd ~

Coming alive with the rise of the moon
and the spells you have cast upon me
further developing who I am meant to become
while retaining my enchantment and charm
to rise before you
fulfilling every dark fantasy
you shall conceive
and request upon me

May 3rd ~

I entered the room knowing the decision to let you crawl through my soul and touch my body was most likely a bad decision. But I whispered to myself, "fuck it," as I walked over to you lying on the bed before me. You have already infiltrated my mind, and I cannot get you out of my heart. Both of which are more dangerous than letting you touch my physical body.

May 4th ~

I envision the strength of your hands caressing my cheek gently, stroking my hair while pulling it just so. I envision your fingers tracing the side of my ribs and down over my hips. Then lower still as I open myself up, inviting you in. I long for the day we share the same space. When we can expel our energy onto one another with my body beneath yours.

May 5th ~

I had to have you, to touch you, to embrace you
In those first moments, time was suspended
A tender, trembling tide rose and fell
as waves of delight strongly surged,
Echoing through our veins like the sweetest wine
Our desire danced, entwined in pleasure
as time stood still but raced by quickly
as we surrendered to the fiery symphony

May 6th ~

In times of adversity and facing uncomfortable moments,
separate and together. You have become my lifeline, my
closest confidant, my friend, my person.

Not only do I desire to kiss every ounce of your soul, make
love to your body, want to be the person you turn to when
you're happy, when you're down, and when you need a
creative outlet, playtime perhaps. I just want to be there.

I hope you will always let me. Always trust what we share
and are courageous enough to join me in the wonderland
we continue to etch into reality.

May 7th ~

I would love you here with me and your lips on the back of my neck, fully feeling the warmth of your breath lingering across my woken skin. Becoming fully aroused as you caress my body with your freshly moistened lips.

I turn my head to the side, giving in and consenting to belong to you fully and you only. You enter me roughly from behind, grasping my face to watch my eyes speak, revealing all the pleasures you are delivering to my body and soul.

In that moment, as we cement our lives together, longing to be by each other's side for eternity and a day we realize how much we have impacted one another. At the culmination of both our bodies releasing and reaching such an intense and intimate climax, I whisper in your ear,

"You are all mine, all fucking mine. Is that clear?" as we feel the throb and wetness spread from our passionate union.

May 8th ~

Tease my mind before you touch my body
Love my soul before you kiss my lips
Gaze into my eyes before you hold my hand
Hold me tightly in bed all night before you love me forever

May 9th ~

It's simple, I want to be desired. I want to be chased even after becoming yours. I want to hold your hand and kiss you in public, during the day, and blissfully under the moon.

I want to be eternally yours, developing a love and passion that satiates both our physical and emotional needs. I want the sparkle and fire always to be lit in your eyes when you look my way, undressing me long before we even touch. I want you to have a thirst that is only quenched by me, and you become parched moments after you drank me in.

I want you to want me, and only me. And I will become everything you desire; confidently stand behind you forevermore.

May 10th ~

Sometimes a moment of pure courage
is all it takes ~ a message, a chat,
a deep invigorating conversation,
and a step out of your
typical comfort zone
Life delivers you a gift,
a friend to cherish
and a connection you didn't
even know you were missing
Life is too short
not to risk it all

May 11th ~

Inherently you knew how to ignite a passion
that rages like wildfire through my soul
without ever laying a finger on my body.

Within minutes,
I was yours all over again.

<u>May 12th</u> ~

She is finally free and needs to play
To her, rules are meant to be broken
and the world is full of grey areas
Boundaries are meant to be pushed,
nudging the bear is becoming amusing
She smirks and smiles with her eyes
raising a brow while scrunching her nose
Laughing, throwing her head back in a wild fit
Pheromones of transgression ooze from every pore
as she blows you a kiss with her dark crimson lips
Her knuckles bleeding, in an attempt to control,
trying to tame the beast hidden within
But she has no use for any kind of penance
no fear of pain and eternal anguish,
confinement will not commence
as long as she has the power
Her rampage and liberations are a choice
certainly not considered sinful
in her almond, hazel eyes
There is no chance of her
being caged once more

May 13th ~

There it is, on display for all to see
my heart within the pages of your soul
Forever etched in the most beautiful way
Touching the lives of many, but mostly me
Our love will be eternal and never shall we escape
the memories we created and equally shared,
so please my dear be aware and fully prepared
A muse I have become, an obsession of sorts
wouldn't have it any other way, but to transport
you and me both to another place; another time
to be together, complete and divine.

<u>May 14th ~</u>

How would you paint me if I was up close
or even from such a distance?
How would you color my soul?
Would it be a reflection to match your own?
What would be expelled onto my skin
to display how you feel deep inside?
Putting all your feelings for me
into a visual representation;
what colors would you use to create
a tangible display for all to see?
Would you use red for love or anger?
Or yellow, for the immense happiness we share
and laughter that never ends
Or black for the darkness that resides in us both?
Or white for the purity of our friendship?
Or pink for an intense budding romance?
Or blue for the sadness that ensues at times
we cannot control despite our best efforts?
Would you stroke your feelings soft and gentle
only to be washed away when the new dawn breaks
or rough, etching them forever into my
tender skin; leaving your mark permanently forever
on my soul as a reminder of our connection?

May 15th ~

Standing before you, skin to skin,
Expelling my sweet scent onto you
My untethered essence
wickedly driving you insatiably wild,
consuming your thoughts;
imprinting on my body
and soul forevermore.

May 16th ~

As you lay in bed, stroking the side of my exquisite tender
arm, your hands begin to explore, caressing the edge of my
black lace panties and finally cupping my sweet exposed
cheek in your strong, firm hand.

Your fingertips gently feel my soft skin and arouse me with
the slightest slow touch, then in contrast, smacking me
firmly, just enough to leave a faint mark for me to
remember you by in the morning.

May 17th ~

After igniting a desire and inherent need for your touch, you take those exquisite fingers and insert them deep inside me, feeling every ounce of pleasure you are creating within my body at this moment. I am wet with desire, ready for more, ready for you to devour my body and claim my soul.

May 18th ~

Enthrall me with your tantalizing, bewitching words, thoroughly enticing me night after night with your mesmerizing, spellbinding thoughts and words you whisper into my ear.

Darling, I am no match for your hypnotic, titillating magnetic lure, but I will show you my charming, charismatic appeal, and you will follow me to the end of time, falling deeper in love by the day.

May 19th ~

I assumed this was going to be an innocent, friendly evening, but I admit, there was a part of me that hoped I was wrong. You were quite the gentleman from the beginning and always have been. You were gentle with my heart, assessing the unspoken signs but acutely attentive to my needs as a woman.

There was a moment when I caught your eyes staring at me from across the room when you thought I was not paying attention. I knew by your look. Those playful, flirty intentions were changing as dark thoughts of us began to swirl within your mind, calculating the mysterious situation, and desire was now written all over your face ~ the decision was made.

The energy shifted between us as your hands became magnets, attracted to my body, to the unknown, not containing your thirst any longer. You began exploring covered places, lifting my skirt, taking charge, firmly holding me in place, and finding every warm, wet place to slide your fingers into with sensual force and tasting every drop of my soul.

I became lost in the magic you created, the seduction of satiated pleasures, and experienced immense pleasure through the enjoyment of exploring one another in forbidden places, leaving no place on our wanton bodies untouched or unmarked. Inherently, I knew I needed this, wanting you to want me. You became the forbidden fruit that I desperately needed to consume, expelling salacious desires and deepening our connection, mixed with enormous respect for one another and unconditional wanting. Our intimacy, inside jokes, communicating with a look, and devious thoughts that we inherently know are just the beginning as we explore the idea of not labeling what this truly is and entails.

You managed to put this girl in her place. A place that most people only dream about putting me in ~ which was face down ~ under your full, explosive, dominant control.

<u>May 20th</u> ~

As you take off your shirt, my eyes focus intensely on your shoulders. I am enamored by your form and game. You became a panther on the prowl, stalking its prey. Expertly crawling your way on top of me with care and passion, thoroughly ready to seduce and devour me, the playful little kitten beneath you.

<u>May 21st</u> ~

Writing together and baring our souls,
bleeding ink spills from every pore
Laying our life out to one another
on pages, through words, like none other
You touched my soul
in ways no one has ever done
I look forward to the day
I could claim, unlike anyone
Searing my name
upon your very chest
you by far
will always be
the very best

May 22nd ~

"You are absolutely beautiful," he said in a whisper.
How I long for the day he is able to say those words into
my ear up against the kitchen pantry door, inches away
from my face.

But for now, the anticipation of his hands and lips touching
my welcoming body, waking me from a peaceful sleep, wet
with desire and throbbing with pleasure, invading every
thought, every desire coursing intensely through my body.

May 23rd ~

Give me all of you, I want it all
I want to love every part
the parts others see
the parts you hide
and have safely tucked away
beneath the surface;
stripping and barring your soul
to only me
We are finally home
and found each other again in this life
Together now, always, and forever
Marking each other for eternity

May 24th ~

Even the strongest women get overwhelmed. But you, seemingly, just know when that is about to occur ~ knowing the words I utter to hint when I just need you to be there. Relaxing my body as I hand over myself, entrusting you completely. Placing a lace blindfold over my eyes, you take control, settling my soul and body. Igniting my senses but instantly calming my mind, and me offering complete trust as you taste and expel every last drop of anxiety from my body. I am becoming the most vulnerable I have ever been in your presence, melting into your hands naturally and with ease. I want every part of you and give you every piece of my soul.

May 25th ~

Laughter
is an
enormous
part of my
life ~
Which is why
I have a huge
need for
you in it

May 26th ~

Tie my hands
with the softest silk,
blindfold me with care
While you gently begin
teasing and kissing my toes
slowly making your way
up to my inner thigh
while the harsh sting
of your bite settles in.

I am yours
for the taking tonight
enter me completely
slowly at first
then show me
who is ultimately
in control during these
moments together.

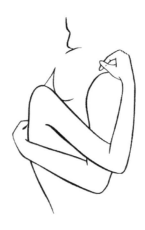

May 27th ~

Unveiling unknown emotions to you
but petrified to share; to be completely
and totally vulnerable; translucent
You have become an enchanted love
a mythical embrace. We are
always moving forward, a complex pair
We are an intoxicating fusion
of longing and grace as our lips
do the speaking of intimate desire
A kiss so profound as two souls collide
No words are needed to fully divulge
what you mean to me now, truth be told

May 28th ~

Desire soaked my satin sheets
as evidence of salacious indiscretions
saturated my soul

May 29th ~

Every moment with you has been a discovery of who I am, who we are becoming together, and where we are meant to be. You feel like a warm Sunday morning at home full of comforting hugs and delicious embraces. And in contrast, insatiable nights tracing your body with my tongue, feeding every desire while memorizing every decedent morsel of your skin. Knowing precisely what you need, driven by an instant connection but feeling like I have known you forever. Falling in love, again and again, night after night, for all time with you.

May 30th ~

The life of an extremist is not always roses, rainbows, & unicorns ~ sometimes, the thorns poke through the expertly crafted facade. I'm just having a night. It's always the quiet moments you need to worry about. I can be brutally honest when I'm okay… but when I'm not, silence overtakes my voice, and darkness hijacks my thoughts - blinding my eyes to the light radiating around.

Who I thought was guiding me, the one to have my back, the one behind me - loving who I am deep down, was ultimately the one to pull the carpet out from under me. Sometimes, without even knowing. Internally I am combusting while my reality is business as usual. I was asked, "Are you okay?" and initially, my response was, "Yes, I am fine." Message sent.

Then I messaged back seconds later with, "Actually, no. But I am not sure you can do anything about it." And that was the end of my communication for the night. So, I sat in silence as I numbly made dinner for everyone else.

Hopefully, tomorrow will be a better day. Hopefully, tomorrow, my coffee won't spill. Hopefully, tomorrow, the carpet will be carefully positioned back, gently wedged under my soul, with an understanding of how the abrupt removal affects my heart.

Having extreme feelings is a gift and a curse. Tonight, it is more of a curse than a gift.

May 31st ~

What if I needed to go to avoid withering away ~ to avoid drowning in this existence, to avoid a life that is not meant for me? What would happen if I extended my hand to you and asked you to join? Would you come? Would you leave your comfortable life? Would you not look back? Or would you choose never to see me again? To simply let me go to leave and fly without you? Could you live with that? Which decision would be yours?

June 1st ~

I crave for you to taste me in the dead of night, waking me gently and marking my body, claiming me for your own; our touch is driven by our intense connection and needs to be deeply intertwined. I welcome and invite your loving, firm touch and will cherish the lingering memories painted across my skin for your pleasure and for me to remember every moment in your arms.

June 2nd ~

Despite the wolf's thick skin and his ability to never let anyone penetrate his exterior walls, he had no chance; he never saw me coming. I was the one that blew his fucking door down, taking up residence in his once-guarded heart piece by piece.

June 3rd ~

Forever walking hand in hand
with all his demons;
she will always hold his heart
safely in her loving hands
Making sure he had everything
he ever desired, wanted, and needed
Whatever that entailed,
whether it was pleasure, softness,
control or wicked sinful desires
Knowing she will always stay,
making sure he was loved
with all her heart.

June 4th ~

I am a little bit of,
"Yes, Sir"
mixed with, "Good boy.
Now please lay back."

I can become your biggest adventure. . . if only you will let
me.

June 5th ~

From the beginning,
You asked one thing of me
~ to stay ~
I believed in you
with every morsel
of my soul and stayed
withstanding every storm
soaking in every rainbow
never losing faith
that I was yours

June 6th ~

I look at myself in the mirror, and there I stand
Reflecting on all the trials and tribulations in my life
that got me to where I am today
someone once asked if I could go back would I?

I gently put my finger to their lips to quiet their voice,
realizing at that moment that every lesson I learned along
the way brought me here, to this very moment

"So, would I want to go back in time? Absolutely not.

I would not be who I am today. I would not have had each
experience, each love, each heartbreak, each joy, each
sorrow. The only regret I have is not finding you sooner.
You are the yin to my yang and the piece missing from my
complex puzzle. Oh, how you have been missing from me
for far too long."

June 7th ~

Somber is the day
rain falls from the sky,
wanting to take flight
or simply nothing at all
I want to crawl under covers
and escape the dreaded doom
but I can't, SO I won't
I have too many things to do
So I instead, pick up the pieces
continuously moving forward
always being by your side
still sparkling with a smile

June 8th ~

You are an unexpected ripple in my life, and I am
obsessively addicted to you ~ you entrance me, and I am
different - more myself with you than I am with anyone in
my life. We are wickedly wild together, dancing through the
darkness where others dare not venture to go. I can't get
enough of your smile, your arching eyebrow, your eyes,
your hugs, and your bite. You are not scared of the woman
I am, and I promise not to ever leave the man you are.

June 9th ~

One by one, unbutton my soul, leaving no place untouched, leaving no place unkissed. Ravish me with genuine authenticity, alighting a never-ending need for you, for us.

The best part of unconditional love is when you offer a blade to the person you cherish the most and know without a doubt they will never use it to hurt you.

June 10th ~

The faint mark on my neck was all I needed to remember you and the night we shared. Without a doubt ~ you managed to do what no one else could. You marked my body and soul.

June 11th ~

I will never stop trying to make you laugh. I will be who you need me to be and myself all at the same time. My desire and need for you to be happy is deeply engrained within my very soul. Whatever that looks like; whatever that means ~ which is the beauty of giving myself over to you. To be with you in body and spirit.

June 12th ~

Fall into my arms and breathe
Letting it all go, every emotion
Letting me absorb all your pain
Tonight, I will be your strength
guiding you, calming you
being everything you need forevermore.

You and I, laughing in the bathroom, will be forever one of
my most favorite memories to cherish. I was fixing my
lipstick, and you came up behind me, pushing my hips a
little harder into the counter. We became lost in that
moment. You started sensually kissing the back of my neck,
wrapped your arms around my waist, and we mentally
photographed that moment in both of our minds using the
reflection of us. Knowing we had to go, you began tickling
me, and we both erupted into a burst of contagious
laughter, admiring ourselves in the mirror, holding each
other tightly. You are my twin flame, and I am so glad to
have you in my life. What would I do without the laughter
and the feelings you constantly stir up deeply within my
soul?

June 13th ~

Sometimes
within the wreckage
of existence
you find the one purpose

And at the end of the day, love is love. Love should be
without labels, without judgment, and universal for all. Love
should be all-encompassing and full of authentic
acceptance. Love should not change who you inherently
are, but embrace every morsel of your soul, only adding to
the love you have for yourself. Loving someone should be
full of pride and truly valid in its own way. Love is whatever
works for you, only making sense to those involved ~ no
one else's opinion is wanted or needed. Love crosses
invisible boundaries and should touch you deeply, forever
caring for your heart and soul.

June 14th ~

You are the missing piece ~
The moment when
you unexpectedly find
the last piece of yourself
to finally feel whole
~ you ~

June 15th ~

After an exhausting, tough day this is all I have the strength for ~

"Am I highly independent? Yes.
Can I handle tough shit? Also, yes.
Do I always want to be that person that can handle it all?
No.
Will I be that person, if needed? Yes, of course ~ because I love him, unconditionally."

June 16th ~

How do you feel knowing you make me so wet, so aroused? Even the anticipation of you turns me into a spiraling feral kitten awaiting to be touched. My body reacts to you in ways it never has with anyone else, ever. I immensely love that about you, about us, and I also hate knowing you are so ingrained within me that I couldn't walk away if I tried.

Do you like knowing I crave your touch and drip at the thought of seeing you, talking to you, sliding myself down onto you? I love it when you feel the wetness you have created when we're together. No one to date has affected me as mentally and physically as you have. Our time together has certainly gotten better, deeper, and more meaningful over time.

I love hearing your voice full of pleasure - seductively, passionately, whispering in my ear how you feel as you pull my hair back and skillfully push my hips down, thrusting deeper into me, taking me, kissing me, connecting as you unload, releasing yourself inside me, claiming me again and again as your own.

You are my greatest addiction, that I never want to recover from in so many ways.

June 17th ~

The first time your lips kissed mine, it felt like you were finally welcoming me home. Our souls find their ultimate match, fitting perfectly together. Rescuing one another in return.

June 18th ~

I remember you once saying . . .
The devil doth bare no sin
like what I envision of
doing to your welcoming body
behind closed doors ~

What sinful, sinister longing and deviant desires do you have planned for your kitten tonight? My body is begging for petting and arousal. My body is begging for the touch of your tongue. My body is begging to be bitten, licked, and kissed in places that would make your momma blush on Sunday morning. Please don't make me wait too long, I will be melting in waves of mental euphoric pleasure. I will be waiting for you to release me, relishing in full liberation of self, discovering who I am, and basking in glorious femininity under the spell of your touch and guidance.

June 19th ~

I am not a subtle creature. When I go for it, you'll know. When I tell you how I feel, you'll hear my words not as a whisper but as a roar. They will deeply resonate within your soul and affect you immensely every day. At least, I hope they do ~ I want nothing more than you in my life.

I hope you think I'm magic. I hope you cherish all the time spent with me and would never consider anyone else to take my place. I choose to spend my time with you. I want and love to see your eyes twinkle when I say something funny. I want to see your smirk when I tell dark, inappropriate jokes. I want to see the anticipation in your eyes when I begin to take the straps of my shirt down off the shoulders. I want your hand to stop me because you want to strip me and expose every last drop of doubt to assure me of your love, of your devotion to me.

I am not for the weak, I require a lot of attention, but I would not still be standing in front of you if I didn't think you could handle me.

June 20th ~

My breath halts
Instantly, taken by you
My focus undivided
Feeling every minute sensation
Every morsel of your soul
Against my skin
As you work your way up my inner thighs
Consuming parts of me
That I did not know could be felt
Never before releasing all of myself
unto but one ~ you.

SUMMER

Playing With Fire

Part 3 ~ Summer

I think it's important for people to know how you feel about them. Whether you express your thoughts and feelings through written letters, a conversation, or looking deeply into their eyes to say everything, your voice is too afraid to speak, sometimes too afraid to acknowledge. Life is too short not to put yourself out there. Life is a journey that is worth stepping out of your comfort zone and undocking the boat from safety. If you sink, well, swim to shore and find another boat over and over again. It is imperative to keep trying. Summer is full of heat and could become a little spicy. Emotions are raging and love is just within reach, scratching at the surface, trying to break free.

"And despite it all
we continue to exist and grow
Learning from the past,
accepting that we are
intricately interwoven,
perfectly planned.
Navigating our existence together
but separate"

~ Tegan Matthews

Playing With Fire

June 21st ~

Taunting and teasing with games of pleasure, leaving you
with lingering desires building within your most inner erotic
fantasies. But you, my unmatched opponent, always
managed to flip the script seamlessly, and I was the one left
breathless in the end, begging for more. Checkmate, in our
delicious back and forth. I am becoming completely
untethered, insatiable for your touch and release while
holding you deep inside. I was yours, and we both knew it.

June 22nd ~

I beg you to caress me without hesitation, harness, or
inhibition, longing for you to entrance me. I am submissive
to your desires; I am yours for the taking to devour tonight.
I am waiting for your hands to entertain my body while
setting my soul on fire, Holding my breath as desire takes
over, pulsing through every part of me. I pause and notice
you intensely staring back into my longing eyes.

June 23rd ~

Play with my body, manipulating my senses, making my heart race with excitement. Persuade me to beg and ache for the pressure of you against me, inside me, feeling the release and wetness between my legs.

No one has ever captured my attention and wants like this, inherently needing you to consume me again and again. I finally found my match, and there is no going back ~ as I extend to you, my other wrist to be tied.

June 24th ~

I usually don't miss a trick. Sometimes it's a bit of a curse. I don't miss a vibe, an energy change, a nonverbal clue that things are changing for the better. . . or worse. I can see it in your eyes. I can hear it in your voice. I can just sense it, sometimes even before you admit it to yourself or acknowledge the impending change in your soul. If you think my ability to craft words and stories to suck you in is a gift or my ability to seduce you into my invigorating and deep, compelling, enthralling worlds where you can reside is brilliant, then you should be aware of me in person.

I'm an addictive drug to many and a hard habit to quit. Do I do this to myself? Perhaps. Do I mean to suck others into my all-consuming energy? I don't know, but I have learned to tone it down to try not letting that happen too frequently. I have learned to keep my distance because if you are caught in my web of desire, you will certainly be devoured whole before you even realize there was a danger to avoid, to begin with. You will be forever mine.

June 25th ~

I realized I was yours before I even knew you as I forevermore wrapped you in a tight embrace against my raging emotional body. This started as an innocent hug, but I took your hand in mine and pushed your fingers deep inside, moistened with my sweet essence, touching my soul. You must make love to my mind while fucking my body, satisfying every need of ours without breaking eye contact for one moment.

♡ *Lover*

June 26th ~

I gently touch the outside of your leg, letting my fingers trail up the side of your thigh and slowly make their way to the inside. I feel the edge of your panties and linger there for a long moment as you begin to arch your back and try pushing yourself closer to me. You begin to roll your hips - hoping my finger slips in to feel the wetness and the anticipation of the evening ahead. What you don't know, darling is this is going to be a very long, slow night for you. I will create many peaks before I allow you to release fully all over me.

I kiss the side of your face, making my way over to your lips as you breathlessly whisper, "Enter me, please - I have been waiting for you all day." You were almost begging. You are, without a doubt, ready, but I am not. Tonight, we will go slow, I remind you, and the build-up will be worth the wait; the climax will be one you will not forget. The art of total seduction had begun hours earlier, and you were waiting, ready, in position, when I got home.

I slowly let my fingers play and enter you, touching the outside of you first, spreading the wetness all over, and then abruptly entering you. You are mine at this moment, but I am not ready for you to explore just yet, as I pull my fingers out just as quickly as they entered. We will have a fun game of edging you just to the brink of pleasure all night long before I finish the job, and you explosively release, feeling the most powerful, intense pleasure before we begin again.

June 27th ~

I am not here to change you. I mean, who truly wants to be changed by anyone? Is that even possible unless the work is put in and you change yourself? My fear is that you will unintentionally change in the process of finding us.

Actually, if I'm being honest, I feel in my heart you have already changed. You are realizing you need more out of life; you want more out of the time you have left. Things that excited you in the past now seem lackluster, and elation does not feel like it once did since I came along.

I know this because, in quiet moments, you think of me, whereas, before, you did not. In quiet moments, your mind wanders, and life with me floods your senses. This is not only true in those quiet moments though, because in loud moments, you also think of me, and that solidifies your desire to be in my presence ~ which I desire and want, need like the air I breathe. But I want you to genuinely be here for you. . . not solely for my benefit.

So, while I am not here to change who you inherently are, I have shifted what you want from life. I have managed to change the trajectory of what you used to think you wanted. While the end game may not even be me, you now need more than you've had. You now need to feel more than you felt with others in the past, and now you need more than someone simply there to just please you and provide pleasure. You will need something real, something I may only be able to give. Perhaps the change in you is just a direct correlation to me and my presence because you have loved me since day one.

June 28th ~

As you assert your dominance over my innocent, submissive ways, you had no idea what was in store for you in return. While crawling inside my thoughts, learning how to control them, satisfy me, guide me, harness me, pleasure me, you were getting lost in my brilliant persuasive mind and my keen eye for detail, and in turn, becoming submissive to my delightful, loving, tender touch, my intelligence, and ultimate desires I had in mind for you all along.

June 29th ~

As I became increasingly more curious about your world, I began asking questions to find out what makes you tick, what dominance drives your needs, what makes your mind spin and ooze with desire and creativity; carving out a space just for us.

June 30th ~

As you undress me firmly with your teeth, you demand the focus of my mind, insisting my eyes never leave yours while communicating without a spoken word; sinfully unveiling our deepest desires and emotions. In these silent but loud moments, I relinquish all parts of myself to you only, forever and always.

July 1st ~

As the red string wraps tighter around my finger, the intensity of my draw to you is overtaking my thoughts and world. You are very much invited, wanted, and perhaps destined. One moment, you are kissing me gently, stroking my cheek, and the next thing I know, I am up against the wall, feeling the pressure of your body against mine. Thoughts of you forever flow through my mind and ignite my body on fire. I have spent eternity searching through different times and places to find you and our connection. Please always stay close to my heart and your hands pressed firmly against my body.

July 2nd ~

As I look up into your eyes, my lips still pressed against yours; I wonder how we arrived here. Feeling your hands firmly around my waist, manipulating my body for pleasure, I melt into you. Inherently knowing you are in full control, but I trust you completely. Blinding my eyes to block out and contain overthinking that haunts my thoughts are welcomed. Tonight is for enjoyment, and you will ensure it is deeply enjoyed.

Tonight is for primal urges to be satisfied, inhibitions to be set free, and fully immerse ourselves in lustful desires. I look to you for comfort while you ravish my body and ignite my soul on fire. I look to you for guidance and completely hand myself over.

July 3rd ~

The music she loves
leaves imprints on his soul
There was no going back
her scent
her voice
her words
forever infiltrating
his mind, thoughts, and body.
She became,
what you would say,
his obsession

July 4th ~

Fireworks exploding in the midnight sky
Your hands gently touching my shoulders
tracing my back with your fingertips
memorized by my silhouette
remembering every tiny detail
I lean in against you
feeling desired and loved
warmth consumes me
as darkness spans the water's edge
life spins all around us
the night busy with energy
but we are hidden as time stands still
In those moments I vividly remember
the sweet smell lingering in the heavy air
engulfing us, wanting it to last forever

July 5th ~

As I drift off to sleep, all I think about are your eyes burning through me. Watching me want you, all of you. Wanting every part, the surface, and parts, you do not show willingly to others. And you, fully knowing the buried parts of my soul that I hide away so very well.

I envision the strength of your hands caressing my cheek gently, stroking my hair while pulling just so, running your fingers along the side of my ribs and down over my hips. Then lower still, longing for the day we share the same space and energy. My body beneath yours. Me with you, and you with me. Watching the snowfall as the sunrise transports us away, even for a brief moment. Fulfilling every life desire and need. I am yours to cherish forevermore.

July 6th ~

Right before you commit to kissing my lips, magic, and mystery fill the air. I bite my bottom lip in anticipation. My eyes are wide, giving you full access and consent to devour the deepest parts of my soul. Breathing heavily or not breathing at all, it seems ~

I stop, pause, my heart racing.

All my thoughts seemingly dissipate, and I give myself over to you once and for all. Lost in your touch, all my churning chaos is calmed.

July 7th ~

She felt safe and guarded in his domineering presence. He was a source of calmness within her turbulent mind that ensued daily in her world. When direction was needed, she learned to turn to him and ask for help. Help that was offered without question, almost instinctively. He would pick up on her indecisiveness and would simply choose for her when she could not.

In turn, she willingly gave him the keys to her unlocking. Her innocence caught him off guard as they shared intimate details about themselves. Waiting for the day when he peels every last layer from her guarded heart, fully releasing her in unimaginable ways.

July 8th ~

I want more, I want different. I am never quite satiated by what I have. Possessions do not inherently satisfy me; it's your soul. Your soul is what I crave. Your attention is what I demand. Your lips are what I need to taste, what I thirst for, and your blood is what I hunger for. If you feel you cannot give me your all, walk away before it is too late.

July 9th ~

Don't make me beg
for your attention
I am willing to wait
for you on my knees
satisfying every desire
you imagined of me
Feeding your cravings in
December with my
submissive May heart.

July 10th ~

Torn from the carriage
carrying death, himself
crawling back
unscathed
conferring
confiding

July 11th ~

I am entranced as you etch wet, written words in my aching
skin, every pore screaming, crying out in harmonious
moans for more. I want you to write your love all over my
body for all to see so I drip with incandescent evidence,
permanently saturated by your eloquent elegies.

July 12th ~

You scare me ~
You are that 'wild card' in my life
as much as I am that to you
It's in the eyes that you see the soul
and I see you ~ knowing who you truly are
Will you wake one day in the future
and wonder what are you doing yet again?
You opened Pandora's box
rubbed the bottle the right way
plucked me out of the toy box that was shut
But are you ready . . . really ready?
to merge our worlds
or will you run and hide
getting scared
Am I too complex?
Do I challenge you
too much?

July 13th ~

Somewhere between chaos
          and midnight
is where the authentic me resides
               & hides
Hidden from plain sight
Hidden from most
Only revealed
to a select few ~
  to see
        to know
              to touch
      to bed
If you desire to know
          my wicked soul
Be prepared to dive deeper
than ever before, playing no games
   bringing no fear
        into the vast unknown
Only then ~
  will the true me be shown

July 14th ~

Play with my body, unwinding the tightly
woven strings tangled from moments without you
Releasing all inhibitions that guard my passion

Play with my body, making music with my soul
helping me lose all sense of control
Look me in the eyes as you undress me slowly
moving to the rhythm we only know

I just want you ~ now devouring me whole

July 15th ~

In the darkness is where I belong. The darkness that you created for me with simply a tie around my eyes. I want to be kept in the dark, the gift of sight temporarily taken, while you tease my body and entice me slowly.

I want to feel you trace the side of my face and grab my hair, pulling my head back so you have easier access to kiss my neck. I want to feel your fingertips trace down the arch of my spine as we write filthy poetry together, using our skin as the canvas, turning our words and actions into art. I want to feel the thrill of your seduction through my body, creating goosebumps on my skin and sending shivers through my soul. I want my thoughts to wander, to race with anticipation of what is to come before you provide any physical pleasure to my body.

I want you to arouse my mind, to leave me wanting, begging, for your touch. Tonight, I want you to be inappropriately appropriate with me. I am yours to play with. I am yours to love. I am yours to mold eternity, satisfying both our needs and yours to cherish for all time.

July 16th ~

I see you around the corner, standing confidently as chills run through my body. My skin is coming alive as I embrace a sensual delight triggered by you, physically affected by your presence. Your eyes seductively smile from within as I watch the sides of your mouth curve up just so. I notice your inviting lips, and the desire I feel for you only intensifies as the intriguing, flirty look crosses your face in the wake of my unknown attention.

I sit staring, unable to look away. Your energy undeniably pulls me in, as I wonder who is crossing your mind for you to be so engrossed in your thoughts. Who is captivating your attention, your soul . . .

and yet you are completely unaware of the spell that I am radiating around the room, solely focused and directed toward you.

July 17th ~

The keeper of the dragon is raging tonight
fire is spewing, and emotions are brewing
Beware of the scorned in her revenge tonight
she is willing to burn down the ground & everything around ~
lighting the match, not looking back
She is kind and gentle, but when you cross the line
she'll turn a blind eye in the wake
of ultimate destruction and demise
She will finally see the defeated look in your eye
her stare will be stone like a final goodbye
The keeper of the dragon will have the last laugh
when you are running for cover, scared to look back
knowing it was YOU that caused this pain
and for you, her love, to be finally slain

July 18th ~

Never will I question my worth again
Your hands are now invisible against my skin
imprinted invisibly on my body ~ in my mind forever
I remember every touch, every kiss, every hurt
forgetting you is so immeasurably hard
but perhaps necessary
You were more than just a pleasure
More than a convenience
You were my friend
a confidant
a joy
an excitement in my world
A place where I could breathe deeply
You saw me until ~ you didn't ~
so I am choosing to see myself
know my worth
to shimmer and shine

July 19th ~

What secrets do you cover behind the keyhole in your private bedroom door? What life do you hide within the walls of your mind? Who are you beyond what others physically see? What are your truest dark fantasies and ongoings beneath the expectations that are typically expected of you?

I am so much more than what the surface shows. Are you brave enough to dive deeply into the unknown with me to explore? Do you know yourself well enough, secure enough that if you do join me, you won't lose sight of who you truly are when you get lost and wrap yourself around and through my world, fully infiltrating yourself in my delusional created worlds?

I try hard to be cognizant of fulfilling who I am meant to be while living my true self secretly, well perhaps not so secretly if you really looked. I may be your best friend, your co-worker, your lover, your neighbor; I may be the person walking by you in the grocery store or picking out tomatoes right next to you. While I may blend in with the crowd a lot, you should always know I am the one on the prowl and spreading my greatness and my energy all around, especially in the bedroom behind the keyhole.

In those quiet moments, within my safe space, I am exposed and undressing myself, letting you see every vulnerability that I hide from most. You are my friend, you are my lover, my most coveted person, and I have let you see parts of me, the real me, that no one else truly knows.

July 20th ~

Please know ~ that at one point, you were a lifeline to me ~ you were the one until my words fell on ears that were not listening, and maybe they never were. My feelings didn't seem to matter, and I felt invalidated, not heard, or taken seriously. Breadcrumbs were dropped sporadically for me to find my way back to you time and time again. There was nothing but manipulative games of pleasure at my expense. Of course, there was always an excuse, always an apology, but you didn't REALLY understand how much you were breaking my heart, even "unintentionally," as you say. You were my friend, an almost lover, and now you are a ghost, a memory fading quickly. How did we get to this point, and do you even care?

You were the one until you weren't ~

July 21st ~

I want to be by your side day and night. I want to hold your hand and place my head gently on your shoulder. I want to hug you tightly and squeeze you without ever letting go or having to say goodbye. I want to be able to come home to you, face to face, when I've had a terrible day, and for you to make all my cares simply go away. I want you in my space, in my bed, and rummaging through my wildly wicked head. You have been my anchor, my friend, my confidant, my person, and I want to never be without you.
I want to feel your hands on the side of my face. I want to look into your eyes and see all the feelings behind your words. I need and want to sense your energy and absorb your soul. Maybe tomorrow, the South will be calling your name, and you won't be able to stay away. You'll hug me gingerly and back me up against the wall to put me in my needed place, showing me all sides of what makes you, you.

July 22nd ~

Do I think of you and get aroused? Yes. Do I have vivid memories of many intimate moments spent with you? Yes. Do I hate admitting that? Also, yes. Do I think of you when we do not speak for periods of time? Yes. Do I hope you think of me when you are in bed at night (alone or not alone)? Yes, of course I do.

Some of these statements were hard to admit and share with you, but all of this is better said than left unsaid. I love knowing I have a certain power over you. I love it when I position myself on top of you, knowing if I push my body a little harder, a little faster, you cannot stop yourself. I love knowing the tiniest of details about you. I love knowing I have memorized every minute morsel of who you are, what you like, and when. I love knowing your threshold of tolerance. I love knowing when you are on the brink of pleasure, and unless you stop me physically, you will explode inside me. I love knowing that when you are ready to give in to that pleasure, you deeply kiss me. I also love knowing your scent will seep out of me, dripping down my inner thighs for the rest of the day. So I, in turn, will think of nothing but you for hours as I feel you on me, in me. The memories of so many moments together are seared into my memory to be replayed over and over when I miss you most. Your presence is a gift and a curse.

July 23rd ~

As I said goodbye to you the other day, you hugged me tightly and kissed my lips. It quickly moved to a more passionate encounter, and it became hard to leave. You took my ass in your hands and squeezed it slowly as your kiss slowed too. I felt you, the feelings you have for me through your lips, and your desire through your fingers gripping me. I wanted your hands up my skirt on my bare skin, but perhaps the next time. Perhaps I need to take charge a little more and guide your hands there myself to show you what I need and when and where.

What I do know is when we are together, everyone else in the world disappears. The world around us ceases to exist. It is only you and me. It is us. I don't notice the people sitting next to us. I don't notice others around or what they are doing. As a people watcher, this is huge. I am solely focused on watching you. I am soaking in every sparkle emulating from your eyes, every smirk, every move of your hand inching closer to my thigh. I am focused on your words and your lips. I am focused on you focused on me.

July 24th ~

I thought I could be stronger than I have been in the past, but the moment my lips touch yours, I am transported back to the awkward girl that you met long ago. I am a strong woman, but with you, I want to be coddled; I want to be 'your girl'.

I do love that you make sure all my needs and wants are met exactly as desired. I love that I can put my feet up on your lap, and you will stroke my legs (even as you take an important phone call) to reassure me you are still there. I love that even as dominant as you can be some nights, you are sweet and sensitive and feel things deeply. I think - I know you are as much of an overthinker and anxious as I am, but you try not to show it too often. I love knowing your insecurities and how to help you in return.

We are always a give-and-take, and I wouldn't have it any other way. Many times, you are the strength in our relationship, and when you need me, I step up and stroke the side of your face and kiss you gently on the lips to take all your cares away. I wish I could help more and do more, but we certainly have a balance between us, and we know at the end of the day, we can count on each other for anything.

July 25th ~

Tie her tongue
with pins,
and she will
surely
seduce you
with her eyes

July 26th ~

It was a fleeting moment filled with ecstasy, making me
smile & laugh. I was blinded by the flightless feeling you
filled me with, hoping love would prevail and transform me,
but every butterfly dream turned raven-black in my mind.
It was sudden, spontaneous; now everything I dreamed is
dead. Everything became grotesque and heavy,
transformation ceasing to exist.

I was living a butterfly dream
in my mind, but my reality
was a raven's worst nightmare

July 27th ~

Becoming the center of an unattainable world, a world where I do not inherently belong, is not healthy for me and not fair for you. This is especially valid if my presence does not align with your ideals or make perfect sense. I cannot complete who you authentically are deep down inside. Desiring the unknown, the wild card, the one you did not see coming ~ essentially me ~ is not enough if I am not what you truly seek or need, even as intimately connected as we are and will always remain. I am you, and you are a reflection of me.

July 28th ~

Ravage me between the sheets
I am eager and will beg
for your tongue to travel
finding uncharted places
and pinpointing precise locations of pleasure
Ravage me until our breathing is in sync
our bodies are one
and cravings are delightfully satiated
Ravage me in glorious style
creating forbidden scandal
in salacious ways
satisfying every secret desire
Ravage me, before I go
making me blush pink with thrill
while at work the very next day
remembering your talents
from the night before

July 29th ~

Rain showers sadness
on her extreme soul
giving internal thoughts
ultimate control
Writing commences
and overtakes her spirit
guiding her senses,
it's very empiric
Day in and day out
poetry are her pearls
Even though she is
but a quirky girl
She dreams of black lace
and a very slow pace
Savoring sweet moments
dripping with lust
in bed, on the streets
It's certainly a must

July 30th ~

You're right. There's no denying it.

There's no hiding it. It's too late. I couldn't successfully walk away even if I tried.

If I did gain enough strength to physically walk, to separate myself from you, I would endlessly compare everyone in the future to you, to us, to the connection we share. You have seduced this feral being into total devotion.

You have done the impossible and tamed the wild beast within me. There is no going back.

July 31st ~

Maybe, tomorrow ~ the moon will sing but
today I wait for the phone to ring
Your silence is deafening
to my deceived ears
I'm compelled to speak out
but am tired of tears
We are separated by miles
and professional choices
so I'll remain quiet
and silence my voices
Maybe, tomorrow the moon will sing
but today
I'm not holding my breath ~
for anything

<u>August 1st ~</u>

Shall I give you something to obsess over? To think about, to read about? How about some late-night excitement? Perhaps it entices you to the brink of total compulsion? You have set the bar high, my love. . . and I never back down from a challenge.

I most likely will tease you continuously with my words. Hell, if you're lucky, maybe you'll even get a picture or two. I will infiltrate your mind and the thought of me will become part of you, will eternally complete you. You may become insatiable to taste my lips, to feel my skin, to stroke my hair, and to feel me from the inside out.

But let me share a little secret. . . If you are this wanting of me, just imagine how much I desire all of this with you, of you. I have in turn enticed myself with my words of ultimate seduction.

August 2nd ~

Wings broken, shredded, defeated
defecting from the once was
Choosing this moment to dance with the devil
filling my soul with needed comfort
He was the one there
waiting for me to need him
Horns sharp but gentle
enveloping me in seductive embrace
Eyes searing through my tattered soul
yet again wanting to pick up the pieces
of a shattered heart
molding me into his every desire
Consumed with his darkness I blindly follow
hoping I rise or fall ~ forever undecided
I quickly surrender to the monster before me
to make the final call

August 3rd ~

I was thinking of you the other day (as I do most days if I'm being honest) and how our friendship has evolved. I love how completely vulnerable you are with me now and only me. I know the ability to be open and trusting of another with your heart is a new experience for you, but that is what unconditional truly means.

We both could go down in a mass of burning flames, but we won't as long as we continue to offer unconditional love to one another, co-existing - living in vulnerable ways and accepting what is to come with an open mind filled with love.

Never be frightened of me. I am not here to destroy you. I am here to love you unconditionally and forever. You are my heart. You are my soul, twin flame. You are my other half in so many ways. I wouldn't know what to do without you.

August 4th ~

I am a wild tempest bringing
raging destruction in the path of my wake
I am the serpent in the tall grass
just waiting to slither on top of my prey
I am the devil, sometimes ~ in disguise
endlessly inviting you into temptation
My lasciviousness with lust is impure
and I hunger for eroticism
My indiscreet urges, my aphrodisia
for you are eternal and deadly

August 5th ~

Needing to be taken tonight
by your sinful, delicious desires
Inherently you knew I was overwhelmed
requesting I, your masked kitten be
stroked heavily by your tantalizing tangerine touch
of sweet leather caressing my bare bottom,
the inside of my thighs, sending my body
into unbridled euphoric waves of pleasure

August 6th ~

I chose to fall even though
I realized I had it all
I had everything I needed
but nothing I wanted
I felt empty, hollow
shallow, unfulfilled
not understood and often sad
When I hit the ground
lying there, still, unable to move
Wishing it was the end
I was still breathing
It was time to confront myself
and time to pick up the pieces
Time to fill my own bucket
satisfying my own wants and desires
I rise and look out, the world is backwards
upside down, nothing as it once seemed
Perhaps I had what I wanted all along
but was blind to the reality
My head eternally up in the clouds
But now, it was time
Time to shine, time to take a serious look inward
Time to truly see the world in front of me
as it actually is, not my perception of it
Even if I feel like a stranger in my familiar world
seeing everyone and everything
for the very first time
Passion is a powerful gift and curse
Passion often distorts my reality
and despite it all, I wouldn't change a thing

August 7th ~

Silence between us, the ultimate truth
your distant surface conversations felt
heartbreaking but telling
I wish you would see
what you do to me on the inside
I'm tattered and torn, getting lost in thought
of what is real, and what is not
Laying alone in bed so many times
pulling every ounce of strength
I have to get up, not to hide
I am tired
I feel like a broken record just spinning
asking and giving a glimpse of perspective
This morning I wake you are silent,
perhaps oblivious and haunting silences
are now eating me deep inside
Not knowing what the future holds
passing the baton over to you
you will either rise or at some point
I will not look back
my head held high knowing I tried
Maybe I was just not enough

August 8th ~

You messaged me at lunch and asked me to have my hair braided and wait for you in our special room after work.

I knew it was a hard day for you. I knew you needed a release. I knew you needed to be in control. I knew what you needed. You didn't even have to explain. I knew you would be as gentle as possible. I trusted you with all my heart. I also knew you would be late. I knew I would be waiting for you on my knees, with my hair braided, in the most spectacular salacious lace panties I had.

I knew, despite the pain, there would be immense pleasure tonight for us both. You would allow me total release, liberation, and a climax worth the wait. . . and you would be able to breathe again after your shitty ass day.

August 9th ~

I cannot stop myself ~
Perhaps it's more like
    I won't stop myself
The fire is already lit and raging, surging
Blood is racing through my veins
        like the most potent, addictive drug
            I've ever experienced,
        a high I begged for, a moment of lucidity and chaos
My desire for you, at this moment, is out of my control
    mounting,
        transforming
            I am becoming obsessive
    The lascivious match was quickly struck, ignited
My lustful thoughts have turned dark and devious
                I am focused on the pleasures I will feel
        before me, because of you, because of us
I have zero regard for the potential burn
        the impending withdrawal, the destructive storm
that my actions may derive
        without the lack or care
            or concern for the imminent fall;
                or the looming consequences
        our entanglement will or could unearth through
discovery,
    Whether real or imagined, I care not
I want to touch your skin, to bury myself within your
mountains
            memorize every crevice of your
                salacious desires and wanton needs
Restraint is not gifted to me as
    I enter the same room as you,

being physically near ~
you are magnetic
and I am compulsive, insatiable
I am full of a lust, I cannot smother
Full of a thirst, I cannot quench
Full of a fire, I cannot control
and full of a desire I will not extinguish
There is no yearning in my soul
to cease my eternal cravings ~
for you

August 10th ~

The queen that I am deep on the inside
why can't you see you are where I reside
Illumination of feelings often told and shared
why do I contemplate if you even care?
The crown has been placed back on my beautiful head
I will not wait around for you to be fed
I will take what is left, tucked in my space,
not to surrender. I now know my place
Until one night, you will be up thinking
what it is I am now drinking
You'll ponder and question, why don't I call
maybe you'll realize it was YOU that dropped the ball
One day I will wake and write without rhyming
about you, about us, about our sucky timing
That day you will know it is far TOO LATE
to be invited back to lick my divine plate

August 11th ~

The tip of your tongue
slowly trailing down my neck
across my quivering
inner thigh
Driving me mad with delight
as you feel wet desire
beneath your fingers
Releasing me
from the chains of reality

August 12th ~

Lightning crackles
illuminating the sky
embracing the chaos
it is time to fly
Rain pouring down
brings danger and torment-ion
calming to my soul
It's time for ascension
I stick out my hand
shake out my wings
It's time, I'm here
birthed, I sing
The demon that became
an angel tonight
wore out their very welcome
in just a fortnight

August 13th ~

Unwanted relics of the past
where the demons doth play
the sycamores bypass
and I should not stay
To the vast unknown
where we all can see
the graveyards & bone
We must all pay the fee

<u>August 14th</u> ~

Stay buried in the past
or keep you around
Digging up coffins
resurrection found
You question,
you ask
what keeps you here
Uncovering truths
of needs my dear
You now must rise
to complete expectation
Because a woman once scorned
is down for the taking

<u>August 15th ~</u>

Blood red roses saturated with confidence
cascade down my sunken frame
covering the insecurities and doubt
thorns cutting deep into my silken skin
war paint streaked across my face
I am ready for battle
on this daunting summer night
haunting screams and nightmares
reverberate through the twilight
walking up to the house
that I once knew so well
I instantly felt like a stranger
where I was welcomed with open arms
now naked, bearing my soul,
I banged on the door
To those on the inside looking out
I am the horned creature, unwanted
estranged from their welcome mat
and inviting fake smiles
I am the devil in disguise
costumed in misery and enviable horns
thick skinned against narratives
that are spewed about me
As I stand there, waiting
I feel a smirk quiver across my face
secretly rejoicing I no longer
have to nod my head in agreement
with their views and conversation
knowing when I turn to walk away
I can straighten my hidden crown
and continue to be myself
standing up for what is right
free and unwavering

<u>August 16th ~</u>

Maybe I had it wrong all along
Perhaps I was the delusional one
I was written off in chapter four
and left to dwell in the silence
discarded, left on read
I just want to know why
I just need to understand
You knew this was the worst
possible fate, or potential
that could ever happen
being abandoned by you
You just disappeared, gone
leaving me no option but
to wait or let you go
with no answers, no conversation
just lingering with all your
exhausting, tired, never-ending excuses
that seem always to come my way

August 17th ~

and despite it all . . .
If you wanted me to, I would sail
through the whimsical
passionate ocean
through the fiery depths of hell
if only you wanted me to
I am not one to beg
for what I deserve,
silently slipping away
with grace, heart breaking in two

August 18th ~

As the breeze blows
windows down
music loudly playing
Endlessly haunted
by inviting thoughts while driving
Wildest dreams streaming
through speakers
Reminds me of many nights
at the waterfront,
red-lipped with you

August 19th ~

Your lips, soft and supple
covered in chocolate
pressed against mine
on this warm summer night
I slowly lick them clean
delightfully tasting you
for hours to come
as I gaze into your sweet eyes
knowing this is where I
eternally belong

August 20th ~

Your sensual touch
lingers on my skin
as our lips lock intensely
yours against mine
Unable to break free
parting only for
needed air

August 21st ~

We're both sitting face to face, in the dark, under the moon. The light brightened your face and I saw your eyes. They are kind, and understanding, and have the ability it seems to see through my soul. We were out in public, leaning against the car, and completely out of control. We both felt a passion unlike anything before, wanting more, needing more. Right at this moment.

You wrapped your hands around my face and I thought you were going to kiss my lips, but you pulled me toward you and whispered, growling into my ear as your fingers found their way up my skirt.

"Darling, tonight you will feel things you have only dreamt about. I want you. I want you to feel me deep inside you. I want you to feel me afterward dripping out of you to be reminded of me all night. I want you to fully be aware that now, you belong to me."

Fuck, I wanted him as bad as he wanted me, and always will, giving him full access to my body, heart, and soul.

August 22nd ~ 12:34 am

I wish I could see you
my interwoven soul
protector, angel
taunting me just beyond sight
I've felt you throughout the years
but what would I give for a glimpse
a night, an hour
I know you're there
always lingering
protecting and guiding when
the clock strikes, filling me with you

August 23rd ~

Always behind me supporting decisions I make, being in my
corner, assisting and guiding, invisibly, protecting me.
Providing a gentle push when needed, a loving caress when
softness is desired while igniting a fire within ~setting my
soul ablaze to embrace and welcome the darkest of desires.
Always knowing what to say, and precisely where to touch
as you look gently into my eyes, seeing a reflection of
yourself, a reflection you know all too well. Creating and
opening my mind to your lifestyle, and your needs.
Teaching me to fully release myself and become who I've
desired to be all along. Walking side by side with me. My
love, my monster.

August 24th ~

Within seconds
my panties were moistened
My body was throbbing
with pleasure
anticipating his fingers
getting closer
to intimately touch me
I wanted him to feel
the velvety essence
he was stimulating
seeping out of my body
feeling his fingers inside me
on the first of many
naughty nights together

August 25th ~

Travel with me
where the masks
are secretly hung
set apart from reality
Tucked away
forever out of sight
for one to forget
all the faces we must wear
to live without regret
Stealing glimpses
of the once was

August 26th ~

Chocolate and chess
Don Julio 1942 awaits us
Anticipating your seductive slow touch
casting me under yet
another spell like no one else
Memories spilling from your lips
dissipating perceived tension with music

You are but a masterpiece
drenched formally in red
Forevermore I paint
the image of myself
back to you

August 27th ~

If you envision
my lips tasting sweet
and succulent, delicious
Let me tell you
a little secret ~

They're full of spice
and magic, pure poison
Please heed my
daunting truth &
warning label
My vivid mind that
controls those lips is dark
and twisted, brilliantly wicked

185

August 28th ~

Tonight I will drink you in, reveling in every ounce of your soul and becoming drunk on desire. I want you to intrude on my body and suffocate my mind as we enter each other's wonderland. We will dive into the dark depths within one another, leaving no boundaries uncrossed or hidden corners unturned. There will just be the intoxication of us within one another forevermore.

August 29th ~

Your voice and your touch
are a powerful drug
to my ears
and you
are certainly
my obsession
in return

August 30th ~

I am the wolf
among the sheep tonight
bucking the system
and realizing I am the
one not vibing with the crowd
In fact, having no desire to conform
awake and aware enough
to see others blindly following along
to the music
to the rules
to the unspoken
cohesiveness

August 31st ~

And so it should be
a mission to find me in lost pages
Eloquently written on paper
remembering shared moments
warm in your arms
embracing last morsels
of energy transferred to you
for eternity
If this was my last poem

September 1st ~

I could cut the intense vorfreude in the room with a knife ~
the tension between us was insurmountably building with
each passing minute. Frisson raced through my veins, and I
could feel your lips kiss my skin, the passion exuding
through your hands before you even touched my body.

September 2nd ~

Meeting you
was not by chance ~ but by fate
What if parallel timelines
existed in our love story
One where we met sooner
One where we reside as only neighbors,
or friends or lovers, or partners in crime
Or the saddest one of all ~
one where we never met
never colliding into one another
never connecting or
finding the familiarity we have
grown to love and count on
That timeline would truly be
devastating to me, to you
and to the magic
we create when together

September 3rd ~

I feel lost without you sometimes
Lost without you in my thoughts ~
without you in those quiet moments
when alone, keeping me company
and a bit on edge
It's silly, really because
it has only been a few days
but I miss you, terribly
I miss the banter, our connection
even the times you tease
and manage to infuriate me
within three seconds flat
I hope you know
how much your friendship
means to me, the girl
on the other end
always waiting

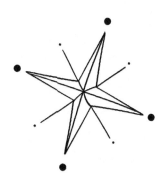

September 4th ~

When your hands,
unaware of the power
they possess ~
unintentionally
but intentionally
brush gently against my leg
my body begins to swell
with pleasure and frisson
thinking about how
you spontaneously
enraptured
my soul last night

September 5th ~

Spiraling through dark depths of chaos
I succumb to the quietness
my voice oddly silenced
as words float through
the abyss of my mind
They are stuck, trapped
not making coherent sense
overthinking
over analyzing
For someone who has
an abundance of words
the unspoken, the silence is deadly
In my mind, waves continue
to crush my soul, getting lost in thought
while mayhem violently ensues
in my dangerous but colorful mind
sinking further still, my swallowed voice
is shushed and my survival is dependent upon
rescuing myself from the void
hoping for a life raft to notice my struggle
and recognize my madness
To notice I am traveling
through a turbulent, invisible sea
and someone to bestow upon me
grace and the courage to survive

September 6th ~

And so I return to a place
out of my comfort zone
outside of my typical world,
A bit more prepared this time
with a lifeline to guide and yet ~
potentially still wearing the wrong shoes
still wearing the same stark white sunglasses
needing to forever borrow a dollar
but still me staying true to myself
fully accepted by you, wrapped in love
and friendship

Thank you
despite it all,
for always being
my friend

September 7th ~

I have a need for more
I'm fully capable
of standing eye-to-eye with anyone
not being scared, confronting challenges
standing up for myself
for what I believe in
But there is a need
to be vulnerable
with just one other person
Someone I can always count on
Someone I don't have to always
be strong with
Someone that takes away
every one of my worries
I believe everyone needs someone
Someone to feel safe with
to be safely yourself
My someone ~
has become you

September 8th ~

There is no roadmap or guide
for us ~ for what we are,
have become or strive to be
However, I do know you are worth
every moment
every cent of the trouble
every risk
every elation
every second together
every longing until the next time
You have managed to awaken a need
I never knew it existed to feel complete
You ignited a raging fire that burns
deeply within my soul for you
Awakened a need of immense desire
to crawl safely into your warm arms
laying my head next to yours
seeing your smile every morning
and endless laughter between us at night
Awakened a need within me to help you
feel things deeply, to be vulnerable
to care about something bigger
and experience unconditional love
for another person, and never settling for less
You are electricity running through my veins
infiltrating my daydreams, and thoughts of you
endlessly swirl through my mind,
behind my closed eyes in the darkness of night
I think about your smile, your eyes, your hands
your lips, your sweetness towards me,
and deviant thoughts

as we navigate this together, discovering our story

What are we willing to risk
for the chance
to have it all?
Everything I hope

September 9th ~

Romanticize every moment of your life
Embellishing, even the mundane
makes life so much more interesting,
like your morning coffee

Envision sipping passionately on a macchiato
like you did last night in bed with a lover,
Letting it trickle down your throat
as you put your head slightly back, lifting your chin
Feel the sweetness running slowly through,
your body, almost touching your soul,
Awakening carnal, lustful needs and desires
Then swallow, realizing the aftertaste is
simply divine as you begin the ritual all over again

September 10th ~

Poets can write about the utmost
lonesome, forsaken journeys in life
magically conjuring expressions
into wildly wicked, beautiful prose
Using words to cut ravines into your flesh
before you ever realize there was a blade in hand
Turning musical harmony into written art
through endless etching of words on paper
Searing marks forever on your soul

September 11th ~

A trail of chills dance across my body, under your fingertips, as you caress my tender, soft skin, where cosmos bloom, senses catching on fire.

My lips water as I'm immersed in your touch, anticipating where you will travel next, igniting, solidifying, deeply ingrained love, and committing your touch to memory. My body knows, without a doubt, you're the one.

September 12th ~

I exist in the magical paper towns of the world
How I wish you were there by my side,
what adventures we would have
But when I wake from my delusions
and walk along the streets of reality
for a brief moment
coming up for needed air
I realize it was a dream, a hope
a desire that never ceases to fade
Even after time passes and days go by
I long to return to the paper towns
I only know in my mind with you
walking beside me hand in hand

September 13th ~

I arrived at the hotel dressed for a somewhat rogue adventure. This is not my typical night-out attire or how I usually behave. But tonight was different; tonight was special. Tonight it would be just you and me and the cocktails that would be flowing between the glasses and our lips. Tonight will be your lucky night ~ I will ensure you get an extra dirty pour from your favorite girl.

September 14th ~

The hallways are dark and inviting
monsters and villains lurk in shadows
around you, biting at your soul within;
invading, infecting every cell
while gifting misery and intrigue
if you dare step into their world

And so you carry on, thinking
what have you got to lose, so you go ~
Looking over your shoulder one last time
proceeding with extreme caution
glancing out the corner of your eye
while searching for a lifeline
before you officially commit

When suddenly the guard
at the gate stops you
ushering you through
with one swoop of their arm
sending you in utterly alone;
this is your battle to slay, your moment
to shine or be buried in the process
Your only option is to move forward
This is solely your journey, you realize
as you take the first step.

September 15th ~

You have been my most coveted masterpiece. Your thirst for control and hunger to experience sexually charged fantasies unknowingly, perhaps unintentionally, called to my wanderlust soul. I needed you to listen to my innermost yearnings. I needed you to teach me about things I inherently wanted but was inexperienced. I knew I needed to learn things only you could show me to achieve what I truly wanted from a partner - a partner to satisfy all parts of my mischievous mind.

So, while you thought I was being charmed and seduced to feed your cravings, it was I that was running rampant uncontrollably through your mind. You couldn't stop thinking about me. You couldn't imagine life before me. You knew I couldn't be replaced. Both of us ruined one another, falling through holes we couldn't get out of easily, and didn't want to; quickly realizing we were the missing pieces in each other's lives.

It was only we who could quench the twisted desires that often wickedly bubbled to the surface. It was only we who could finish writing the most magical story of a love that spiraled into an obsessive need, a fairytale worth telling and sharing. A fairytale that others would envy. A fairytale that we know neither of us would survive independently of one another.

C

September 16th ~

I need you to be
in my physical space
to be in my presence
to look into my eyes and
run your fingers across my skin
I need for you to memorize
every part of my body just
as you have infiltrated my mind

September 17th ~

Are you intentionally withdrawn
blocking me out, or just not caring?
Is it on purpose
or simply forgetting
my perception is overshadowing
the reality of the situation
It feels as though
the space between us
is impenetrable
Perhaps happening
without your knowledge
But still, I sit in silence
this afternoon
staring out the window
wondering
if it is too late to change
Wondering
what you are doing
with your time
at this moment
Asking myself if I
was ever special to you
and who you think about
in the quiet, stillness
of the day

September 18th ~

Knowing you are always there
Knowing in my heart you care about the person I am
Knowing without a doubt I am the one
in your life you can't live without
is the most wonderful gift you can give to me
It allows me to breathe deeply daily
It allows me to be confident in choices I make
It certainly isn't needed, but you are
certainly wanted in my life

September 19th ~

The distance between us
creates an insatiable need
to taste you on my lips, in my soul

September 20th ~

After a night together, I slipped on one of your white button-down shirts, knowing this may be one of the last times I saw you. I didn't want that to be the case, but I felt it deep within, down to my core. I was losing you; well, in fact, you were losing me.

The magic between us has long since dissipated, and the conversations felt forced. There were many minutes of silence between us at dinner; many times I searched through my mind for a topic we could kvetch about - not to complain, but squeezing something out of nothing. I was once entranced by you, by our conversations and outings. You had a way of mesmerizing me, a way of sucking me in. It is heartbreaking that you no longer have that power over me. I liked being little red, led astray by the big bad wolf.

So, for now, I will enjoy this last moment together and soak in every last morsel of your soul tonight. I will be gone in the morning, and I know (at least at this moment - it could very well change) that it will be the last time you will freely have access to touch my skin, explore my mind, and bathe in the brilliance of my soul.

September 21st ~

He turned to bourbon to mask the desire running through his veins as if the alcohol would take away the temptation. We both knew it would only make it worse; harder to dismiss, harder to ignore ~ and so he finally gave in, ravishing my soul in such wicked fashion. The fear of consequence did not matter at that moment.

September 22nd ~

The caterpillar once asked Alice, "Who are you?" Identifying as Alice, looking through the glass, a piercing reflective representation of myself is shown. I am left staring into the shadows, my perspective of reality, wondering who I truly am, placing the impostor aside. Am I the dreamer in a fantasy-induced world floating through carefully crafted masterpieces of my existence centering solely around my needs and desires? Am I the serious apropos overthinker, always one step ahead, considering which road to go down and the potential consequences of such? Am I the lonely pent-up soul finding my way, unsure but oddly confident in each direction I chose? Am I the fun-filled, lighthearted bouquet of daisies I set out to be, full of joy and romanticizing each day, giving wonderment to a life lived? Am I the mushroom, growing in the controlled darkness, spreading spores of misery with ill intention? Am I the dark grey wolf, calculated and intentional, able to cut through hearts with one glance of my eyes if I so choose? Or am I just me, a delightful, dangerous collision of all above, uniquely different while being creatively selective throughout defining moments in my life? I eat one side of the cake to grow my mind and majestically sail through life untouched while simultaneously drinking from the other exquisite bottle before me to shrink and hide before my foes of choosing. Perhaps carefully combining the two for a spirited journey, a quest to find myself while losing parts of me simultaneously. Not really knowing which way to turn, while always inherently knowing the end game.

AUTUMN

Playing With Fire

Part 4 ~ Autumn

The energy in Autumn is unmatched. It's like a phoenix rising out of the ashes, full of personal transformations and empowering you to believe in yourself. This is a time of magic and full acceptance of your authentic self. It is the 'ride or die' season. I feel in season, anything is possible.

"Words I write may never be read by you. Words I feel within my soul are set ablaze, perhaps never to be discovered. I push the limits ~ I play with fire; setting myself apart from you to find myself in the end. Realizing the only way to rid myself of you was to set fire to the once was and start anew."

~Tegan Matthews

Playing With Fire

September 23rd ~

In the quiet autumn morning
usually full of passion and thought
my coffee spills
slowly dripping down the wall
leaving brown stains in the trail of wake
indifference soaks my soul
Today words need to become actions
or lost again, I will be
How can you love someone without
sharing the same space
Energy existing but being
two separate worlds,
residing in one

September 24th ~

Quiet morning moments
forever wanting
to be in your presence
The longing
that overtakes my thoughts
is overwhelming
wanting to be cared for
by you
wanting to be held
by you

September 25th ~

Tangled tongue touches
    between my tender thighs
        You disappear deeply into my lips,
          sliding,
      slippery,
          tasting my tempting,
    piquant, quintessence
I explode under your skilled spells,
        as you write a filthy, salacious love story
      with your talented tongue
            about our sinful discretions
        between our satin sheets,
           forever stained by me

September 26th ~

From the outside looking in
you see acceptance
warm inviting smiles
inside jokes
and neverending love and desire
You see lights and celebration
glances exchanged
and sparks in the air
But from the inside out
I feel longing
neglect
unfulfilled desires
dinners alone
silence
always left wanting more
and infrequent touch
Truth is in perspective
How is one thing seen
but another felt

September 27th ~

Today, I am spiraling into a negative space
a void with no words to offer
No thoughts I can pin down
No answers; simply just overwhelmed
I am fighting invisible anguish and torment,
struggling for truth, I shut down
I feel like a puppet with strings
being pulled and manipulated
Disconnecting from life essentially
Needing time to myself while
the path of destruction
has a plan of its own
and control is not
gifted to me at this moment
There is no way to stop the ball from
rolling off a metaphorical cliff
And so I blindly follow, taken with the wind
fully prepared to greet whatever is to come
Hoping to fall gracefully
without too much injury
to myself or others

September 28th ~

I feel like a giddy schoolgirl with you. We have a silly vibe that quickly turns to edgy when desired. We are both dark and sarcastic with a flair for devilish fun. We have a child-like love, and we never stop laughing and playing, even engaging in distracting games of footies and pleasure under the table during very boring and official meetings.

From above, no one is the wiser of our play down below, but I am thoroughly distracting you to the point of hysteria, and only I know why there is a huge smile spreading across your face. Only I know why your dimples are emerging. Only I know why you need to remove your suit jacket because you are sweating a bit - mid-conversation.

It was me, all me. Me being seductive, secretive, tempting you, pushing you out of a perceived comfort zone and into a place of enjoyment, a place of extreme emotional response, a place within my dark reality and colorful fantasies, a place I didn't have to do too much convincing to get you there. You willingly walked into my arms after the meeting and followed me to a dark corner after everyone had gone. You backed me up to the wall, grabbed my face, and looked at me sternly, catching me off guard.

You secretly enjoyed every moment, but my behavior was a bit risqué, I'll admit. I was certainly taunting you. I was teasing you unknowingly in front of the others. Standing before me in the darkness, you assertively looked into my eyes while your hand grabbed my face around my lips so I couldn't look away. You used your strength to hold me still.

"Don't," you said with strong glaring eyes, inches from my face as you pinned my other hands above my head against the wall.

"But why not?" I managed to mutter through my lips that were being squashed by your strength. Clearly, I'm not learning my lesson and still trying to be playful, trying to smirk through your storm. I did manage to smile through my eyes as I batted my lashes before you.

"You do certainly like to push limits and boundaries, don't you?" You whispered very close to my face, which aroused me even more than I always was by feeling your body up against mine. "This is certainly not the place, doll."

And with those last words spoken, you kissed my lips more passionately than you ever have before. I think you enjoyed my little games this evening. In fact, I know you did. Your body and hands don't ever lie. Your kiss and passion just reinforced my naughty behavior and antics under the table, just out of sight from the lion's watchful eyes lurking in the tall grass.

September 29th ~

Leave the poison aside
it will be there
        when we wake
    for you to continue killing me slowly
        You are deadly
Tonight, I need you to
    spread me wide open
                    dripping creamy, warm
            wet chocolate
    down my thighs,
licking every last drop
            till I scream your name with pleasure
        and not beg for mercy

September 30th ~

A wall built between us, securely erected
and a divide that is growing, connection fading
You are not mine to take time from
but feel you have gifted me that, until recent
Busy are our lives apart and time is all we can give
even for a brief moment throughout the day
Do I not cross your mind in the chaotic quiet?
If I do not, maybe I need to reconsider
which side of the wall I belong on

October 1st ~

Having to do even the
most mundane of tasks,
always turns out to be
the most epic of adventures
~ with you

October 2nd ~

I can exquisitely convey how I feel in my writing with ease,
but when you look at me, your eyes pierce through my
soul, and I instantly shrink and look away.

Why can't I verbally stand behind my writing and
eloquently speak as I write? Why must I be so
uncomfortable when looked at when I am seen?

October 3rd ~

I gifted you my innocence, and instead of nurturing and loving me in return, you handed me a poison apple to destroy every last morsel of goodness in my soul. You knew what you were doing. You knew I would be tempted to follow. How could I not? You were charming and handsome - there was just something about you I could not resist.

There was no way I wouldn't be tempted. And so I went into the woods, alone with you, without a thought that you would be my worst demise, my biggest downfall. You created trust, and when I finally saw you for who you were, I knew I should have listened to all the gut feelings I had and the red flags I tried to bury. I knew you were not for me, and by the time I realized this, it was too late.

October 4th ~

Pull my hair a little harder
as you enter me from behind
Envelope me in satisfaction;
creating a release only you are aware of
Know every ounce of my soul,
every detail of my body,
and how to create such pleasures.
You know all of this
- only you-
Claiming me as your own;
marking my soul with your lips,
branding my body with your name

October 5th ~

I often feel nervous in the quiet moments with you. Unaware of your thoughts and feelings, hiding so much of me but so open it scares me. The moment we first touch after so much time apart, excitement runs down my spine and through my soul. Familiarity rushes back, and calmness overcomes me. Feelings I have been longing for but never finding until now.

October 6th ~

Explosive connections between us, as fireworks burst above,
Illuminating the darkened sky
as we lay beneath the dazzling glitter and
twinkling twilight flying high
Sparks light when your warm, wet tongue
touches my inner thigh
for the very first time
Effervescent excitement bubbling to the surface
My muscles clench, and my hips move as you dive deeper
between my lips, feeling every fold, the wetness
without an ending, without a fizzle
You are electricity in my veins
a drug written, etched with my name
gasoline igniting without a flickering flame
erupting orgasmic screams echo through
only covered by the roar of the dragons
incandescently dancing,
mere lightning in the sky
and the gush that tipped the sea of pleasure erupting
coming out on the other side
You ~ stroking my face
inserting yourself, we wait
religiously for round two
The finale will be the real show
as you look into my eyes,
proud of the reaction
you eternally evoke

October 7th ~

I wrestle with chaotic thoughts,
       thrive off utter mayhem
   and relish in the bedlam before me
Pandemonium speaks to my soul
       as madness runs through my veins
  and anarchy ~
     is truly
        my given first name

October 8th ~

You are living under my poetic spell of sorcery, placed inside
beautifully crafted masterpieces in print unable, unwanting
to be set free, while I, the enchantress transcribes words that
pulls you closer still conjuring lust and love, bliss or hell
depending on the day. I captivate you with every bewitching
thought that is spoken and tucking you gently in my poems
at night when the moon is full. We forever bring life to our
longing that is embedded deep within our souls. You are
forever living amongst these pages, caught between my
fantasies and the real world in which you live. I hope you are
able to see, through my eyes, how much I depend on your
presence, your soothing magic ~ just waiting for the day
when the two worlds wondrously collide. But, until then, we
wait. You are mine to cherish, charm, and guide safely,
cultivating our existence with me alone, loved by you . . .
your heart, invisible to others.

October 9th ~

I am intense. I spend a lot of time dialing back the depth of my existence. My love for living is all-encompassing with child-like wonder and amazement. I have learned when to channel that energy and realize when it gets overwhelming, even for you. I harness my onslaught before it is too late, becomes too much, or too soon.

October 10th ~

Imperfections glorified
Imperfections magnified
Staring me square in the face
One day you are my friend
another you are my foe
Loudly spewing self-hate
like it's written in bold all over my body
Or making love wearing
the most exquisite silk and lace
You capture such perfection in the twilight
Seducing my poignant temptress reflection
Then leaving me to dwell in despair
when the glaring stark daylight arrives

~My mirror ~

knows all my secrets
a living diary, a confidant, and traitor
Imperfections glorified
Imperfections magnified
Perfectly imperfect
I confidently decide

October 11th ~

You're right, I am territorial, which is a bit different than being an envious green-eyed monster, full of jealousy. I just protect what is mine and you ~ you are mine. Please don't forget it, or you will feel the wrath of my once undying devotion and sought-after love. I certainly won't seek revenge. That's simply child's play. I'll just walk away like you don't exist.

October 12th ~

I will tempt you from the first moment we meet. Will you be able to resist my seduction? Will you ever be able to walk away from me unscathed? In the past, not many have been strong enough to resist the temptation of my magic. My spells are powerful and intoxicating, sucking you in from the very start. The first time I kiss your lips and bite your neck, you will be mine without hesitation or a second thought. You will forever be faithful to me because losing me would bring total darkness to your world without a taste of complete ecstasy and satisfaction.

October 13th ～

After an evening out with you, the real pleasure at home is just beginning. We walk hand in hand up the long spiral staircase to our bedroom as you touch and tease, trailing behind.

I stop and stand in front of a full-length mirror, staring at my formal reflection wearing an exquisite white gown, my hair is knotted up, and I am adorning the most delicate jewelry. You come up behind me and trace down my spine with the back of your soft, smooth hand from the nape of my neck to my hips as you slowly, deliberately unbutton the back of my dress. Your lips solidify your love as you kiss the invisible trail you just etched into my skin moments ago.

I let my head lovingly fall back onto your bare chest as you reach your arms around the front of my body, cupping my breasts and hugging my soul. You begin to undress my body and feel your way into my warmth. Anticipation spreads through me as goosebumps develop across my skin, complete with shivers and tingling throughout my body from the frisson you managed to create within my mind.

October 14th ~

Some things in life you actually have to experience to understand completely. There are many things I won't speak of because I have never experienced or don't understand them fully. . . but when I do understand, I am a force to be reckoned with.

But before diving in, ask yourself ~ Could you handle me in the driver's seat? Could you handle me in the passenger seat? And even if you could handle me as a passenger, I'll warn you ~ I am quite the backseat driver. Or try to top from the bottom until you put me firmly back in place. It's just my inquisitive, curious need for controlling nature.

I will be that little voice inside your head, infiltrating your thoughts and running amok in your mind. I am all-encompassing, and I don't leave. Just when you thought the angel was approaching, the devil was steadily on the other shoulder, whispering in your ear, tantalizing you with thoughts of what I would do to you. Eternally tempting you to go to the dark side.

So, please be patient. I am worth it. I am loving and giving, and kind. I am knowledgeable and a quick learner. I also know when I need to listen. I will quickly know if you are worth my time if I can trust you, and if my instincts give me the green light - I will do whatever I can to make you happy. Then and only then will I submit to you completely.

October 15th ~

As I sit in thought, watching life fly by on a warm Saturday morning, feeling the breeze blow the hair off my face, exposing parts of me that I keep well guarded. I am thinking about everything I have experienced; all the choices I have made, my world was once filled with glitter and sparkles ~ I am fixated on color, crafting masterpieces of myself, dwelling in the magic that transpires after dark, energetically dancing the nights away, while getting lost in loud pulsating music and bright city lights, unexplainable vibes were by far the most fun, my favorite ~ until you.

October 16th ~

When you think your story has been written and etched for all to see, a plot twist interrupts the pristinely written wet ink. You are left with a cliffhanger to make choices that challenge your soul and the very essence of who you appear to be.

Are you up for the trials that lay ahead? Of course, you fucking are! You are braver than anyone I have ever met. You are continuously diving deeper into the abyss of life daily and make dancing with your demons look like child's play.

Always remember, the first draft of your story is never final

October 17th ~

Your dimples kill me every time I see you as I look at you across the table. Having coffee and conversations with you in the morning just feels. . . so natural.

I love that you know my coffee order. I love that you always take the lead. You are a gentleman in public, but it is "the you" in private that I obsess over, that I cannot get enough of or out of my head. Our relationship is a bit extreme. We are extremely close friends. Hands off during the day but lovers at night, soaking up every inch of skin as we touch one another's souls.

Sometimes, I will breach that forbidden bridge during the day when no one is looking. Placing my foot on the chair next to you, inching my body a bit closer, or touching you just a tad longer than normally acceptable.

October 18th ~

You looked into my eyes, sitting across the table, and said you missed me. It was an insanely sweet moment. The next thing I knew, my panties were pushed to the side, my face was pressed up against a concrete wall, and your hand was over my mouth to quiet the moans that were escaping my lips as you took me from behind after dinner - in a dark park.

I missed you too. I managed to whimper back. I was a complete, beautiful, sweaty mess before you.

October 19th ~

My feelings are on fire, I need to adjust
untamed, but real, I may combust
Settling the rage in my soul is essential
you may not know - it's evidential
Any of this is actually occurring
Putting a smile on my face
simply soul-stirring
Proceeding with expectation
never allowing you to see
What is actually brewing
beneath the marquee

October 20th ~

Today
I am utterly alone
and accepting
of that truth
preferring the solitude
over fake emotion
tired excuses ~
simply over you
I feel defeated
unheard
unimportant
Sitting in this place
readjusting perspective
ready to rise out of the ashes
reborn, a phoenix
forever rising
forever recreating
picking up the pieces
of myself with added knowledge
becoming even better
than before
but first
I must sit
Alone

October 21st ~

Never again
chasing shadows
of my toxic
former identify
Forevermore
rewriting myself

NO MORE

October 22nd ~

I'm a wild card with black lace and red lips – you never know what you may get from me on any given day. Talk about being a 'switch' – either I will be submitting with oozing anticipation from my hazel eyes, saying, "Yes Sir," with perfect braids cascading down my back, or I am demanding that you lay back and be a "Good boy". (Or maybe it's all because you let this happen, and it was part of your plan all along – knowing I needed to be in control sometimes, and you entertain the idea occasionally.)

I feel my personality, in general, is like this, though. Does one unlearn this eventually or just embrace it? I find myself either wanting to be under you, following every direction precisely, or on top of you, demanding that your every move aligns with what is in my fantasy that evening. Or maybe I am all talk – and when I am in front of you, looking up into your gorgeous eyes, you will easily trump my energy and firmly put me in my place without question or hesitation, respectfully under you.

October 23rd ~

All those times you broke me
realizing I, matter not
Becoming numb
to the hurt spawned,
finally able to mask
the illusory pain
so you do not think I won
Pretending, playing your game
until I can walk away
unscathed

October 24th ~

Deceitfully saddened
dishonesty around and through
Walking deserted halls
eternally, without you

October 25th ~

There is no way I could ever let you go. You have become so deeply embedded into my existence ~

I need you
I want you
I desire you

All of you, with me, forever.

Dancing under the full moon. Listening to music for hours. Taking my hand and leading me to the bedroom. Coffee in the morning and movies in the afternoon. A love story people will envy that simply created itself.

October 26th ~

Despite our worlds colliding at massive speeds into each other, at that moment between us, time stood still; it stopped and froze completely. It is now etched into my soul, and I will never forget lying face to face with you, stripped bare, gifting each other a piece of our souls ~ you are now deeply embedded within me. Words spoken and hidden kisses on our skin, in places that no one else will ever see or know, are forever part of who I am, part of who we are together.

Our journey won't be easy, it won't make sense, but we need each other in whatever ways we are willing to give. Losing you would be detrimental ~ you are forever a piece of me.

October 27th ~

What lingers below the surface? What shadows are hidden deep within your soul, my soul? Carefully, we peel back layers of ourselves, finding who we truly are. Perhaps, finding the one we were always supposed to be with, reuniting with our other half. And as a result, there is no going back. We are different people now than when we began this unexpected journey. Rationally, there was no explanation. Irrationally, it all just made sense.

October 28th ~
(Inspired by Emily Dickinson's, "I Died for Truth")

I died for truth ~ but was it in vain
Always looking to find meaning
behind my once given name
Running out of time, I wanted to see
what was ultimately meant, for dying me

I conferred with beauty across an empty room
somewhat tragic how we place so much stock
in physical appearance, instead of logic
Why not seek truth, before leaving this place
to find why we're here, a purpose, a lesson;
to help others see and simply to save face

To propel forward, facing uncomfortable truths
sacrificing myself to help them reach high roofs
Maybe that's why I'm here, laying my life on the line
while beauty remains in the mortal realm divine

Truths and perceptions are rarely valued
beauty blindly prevails when masks are transvalued
Maybe we're both just fucked in the long run
facing many daunting years of ignorant fun

Left in a room, connected it seems
to confer and obsess without pretentious extremes
and dreams that have failed many times over
If truth and beauty are rare can they exist without one
another

Can I be truthful to say beauty doesn't matter
Our society would disagree, I think, ten times over
We value both it is said, so very much
Truth without beauty is too often overlooked

As we stand at deaths door, what really matters
Being truthful with ourselves always forever
I died for truth, won't take it in vain
I'll trust and support, as long as I'm reigning queen

Death doesn't care, we all have to go
for beauty or truth - it's all unimportant
not placating reality and simply for show
None of us survive, we're all covered in moss
in the ground, in the end so choose to be
your own ~
immortal boss

October 29th ~

Undecided how well-liked I actually am ~ or is it simply my irresistible, provocative eyes inviting your attention, wanted and unwanted. Provocative eyes gleam with joy and spill every dark, sorrowful secret in my soul with one look. I can stay silent, and hold in my thoughts, but every time ~ my eyes are the traitors in disguise

October 30th ~

You're too late. You have finally managed to do the impossible. I've officially learned to live without you. I don't think we're even friends. I know this is accurate when I found out you were struggling with someone else. I used to be the person you could talk to, wanted to talk to, but now I'm just a ghost from your past, lingering and perhaps only haunting you throughout the night when there's no one else to call.

October 31st ~

Chocolate is a
poison,
surging through my veins
driving me insatiably wicked,
wildly out of control

November 1st ~

I needed time away;
a moment to think
to reflect
& all I thought of
was you

November 2nd ~

I've never wanted perfection. I want real. I want
authenticity. I want dedication, honesty, and desire ~
without hesitation, without resolve. I want you to pick me a
million times over. I want it all, never settling for less than I
need. I desire all of you and still crave your presence.

And after all his time, I still want you to see how energy fills
my soul, how sunlight touches my eyes and makes my soul
glow from the inside out. I want you to feel my embrace
and my soft skin. I want to stay up all night talking and
laughing with you. I want to sit on your lap and feel your
hands all over my body.

I want you. I want us. I want the fairytale.
If only, you did.

November 3rd ~

Find me written within the pages of your favorite novel. I want to be your favorite chapter in your most beloved book, not written off in an untimely death in chapter 3. Find me in the middle of your favorite garden or your most adored fantasy. But please know I dwell in extremes and contradictions. And while I want to be the center of your world, I am spicy black pepper and sweet sugary, pink lemonade. I am the most violent of thunderstorms and the prettiest rainbows after. I am the hottest, scorching days in a summer heat wave and the coolest, most relaxing, laid-back days in autumn. I am the life and death of most parties. I love monsters and vampires, as well as pink lipstick and unicorns. I am the darkness and the most brilliant light. When I love, I love hard. I just want you to love me the same with pink lips or black (mostly black).

November 4th ~

I have become a slave to my desires,
consumed with a need to feel
you are racing through my veins
entering all the intricate compartments
in my obsessive, compulsive brain
I need to inhale you, a high I crave
an elation you can only evoke
as you infiltrate my mind,
seeing the world differently
all the fucking time
You are an elixir, poisoning my perception
of reality before me
a potion that necromances
my lifeless soul into an efficacious body
One that I cannot control; I am a slave to it all
The alchemy of this drug creates
the embodiment of gluttonous diversion
an incarnation of the existence, quintessential to my spirit
I need you to feel, to exist, to survive
Doing unspeakable things to keep the aura of you
surrounding me, oozing, expanding
in my blood, coursing through my decent
into pure madness, invisible to those around
I hide it well, functioning with mere perfection
but under the surface, I am drowning
in chaos and gluttony, obsessed by you

November 5th ~

Bravely reminiscing about the trials of my existence. The moments I felt invisible and times that brought me to my knees, crying and screaming for death himself to sweep me away; to take me by the hand and guide me to his sunken eternity.

Reflection is necessary to grow, they say. I want to know who "are they" with all this wisdom. It's often hard to look back to see all that has been discarded to rise. Ambition can be glorious but often a lonely journey.

November 6th ~

Stardust escaped
my fingertips
when I gazed
upon the moon
All I ever wanted
was to be caressed
by your forsaken lips

But my want for an
extreme amorous love
comes second to my need
for emotional stability

November 7th ～

I am unhinged today. This, I need you like this with me. I need your hand between my thighs, firmly gripping, pulling me into you. I need you to grab the pearls from around my neck so there is no place for me to go but into you more, submitting to your desires.

I need you to kiss my lips so passionately that I forget about every terrible thing running through my mind. I need you to take me to places in such an erotic way that I am ruined for anyone else. I am only yours, and I want you to never let me forget it. I need you. I need you in me. I need to feel your hands on my body. I need your fingers twisted in my hair. I need your eyes on me. I need your soul entwined with mine forever. I need you in my life and want you in my space.

November 8th ～

My biggest fear
is that you
will become a stranger
after almost having
it all ～

November 9th ~

She was a timeless beauty, an evergreen, full of eternal life, existing ~ steadfast through the harsh winters and rough moments that often challenged her soul. Her beauty remains constant and immortal, existing even when the birds fly, taking flight, abandoning safety, and leaving for easier, greener pastures. The evergreen remains strong, everlasting, confidently standing her ground, taking on the challenges ahead, with grace and quiet strength ~ never faltering in the wake of dissonant realities ahead.

November 10th ~

I want you. I want you like I've never wanted another. I want you to look me in the eyes as I unbutton your shirt. I want to hear you catch your breath as I kiss slowly down your chest all the way down to below your belly button to wear your pants begin. I want to smell your scent, your cologne left from the day. I want to feel your lips graze my neck as you get lost in the fantasy smell of my hair. My desire for you is raging. It's a hunger I've never felt before. You are my only satiation. You are my only need. You are my only want. You are my craving, and you are the only one who will feed my starvation for physical and emotional intimacy.

November 11th ~

Insatiable intimacies,
dirty thoughts lingering, infiltrating
uncontrollably in my mind
I spot the most intriguing man
across the room
I cannot take my eyes off him
He catches me watching his every move
as insatiable intimate longing prevails,
fantasies unraveling, desires to explode
overtaking my mind, my body and soul
releasing a wild, uninhibited side of me
What I envision between us tonight
would either entice him further
or send him running without
looking back

November 12th ~

I'm tired
of giving
so much
of myself
over to you
with no
reciprocation

November 13th ~

Drowning in chaos, drenched in reality; an unknown
reflection was staring back at me through the mirror. It was
familiar but foreign. Eyes, full of judgment, were searing
through my soul, wondering where the confident girl went
that she once knew. I wondered what it would take for her
to be revived, saved from the vapid waters, and put safely
back on shore to fulfill every dream buried deep within her
soul, my soul.

November 14th ~

When every vulnerability is exposed
within your existence, within your soul
Loving you becomes a blessing
a need, and a curse
You become the air I breathe,
the scent I wear
the thoughts I'm consumed by
Love simply prevails and becomes unshakable,
unharnessed, existing without borders or labels
When two people are connected
in ways others cannot even fathom
magic transpires with great passion,
sweetness, and a powerful story is birthed
from fallen ash and written for all to see

November 15th ~

You've absorbed parts of my soul
and I will never get enough of you
Our hearts quickly connected
as you endlessly listened
about my rigorous days
soothing my soul
and calming my mind
I will always be there for you
whether it's kissing you
sweetly, passionately
being your equal
or submissively under you
A never-ending give and take
back and forth,
transferring of power
seamlessly
I give myself to you completely
as we continue to always
look forward, never back
You have become
~ My forever

<u>November 16th ~</u>

Past dreams, and fallen stars
litter the ground
making space for
your true self to shine

November 17th ~

You have successfully teased and infiltrated my mind ~ I am now begging for you to touch my body. How long will I need to wait? How much patience do I need to develop? Is this all part of your grand plan and education? I'm ready. Please just come and take me. Take me away and play with my body as a good girl deserves.

I am ready for you to braid my hair with care only to destroy it. I am ready for the next level of you with a smirk on my face and wrists waiting to be tied as no one has before. I am begging for you to break me in, teach me, and guide me through many nights of a needed, wanted, and desired education. You are a master at your craft, and I am a willing follower, a lover that will be obedient, letting you lead.

I am ready for you to slowly unbutton the back of my dress, deliberately unlace my corset with care, strip my body bare, and trace all the invisible words on my skin that you have uttered and etched. I am ready to feel you penetrate my body and soul. I am ready. I am begging. I am lustful for you - and only you.

November 18th ~

There are two sides
to every story
to every person

Can they exist
without the other
residing in the same
body of matter
ink penned on paper
thoughts, words spoken?

Can the light exist
without the dark?
Which side is authentic?
Which side is the impostor?
Which side is the true story?

November 19th ~

Cutting into you just to kiss your scars
has become the inescapable routine
I needed to break it, I needed to break free
of hurting you, of hurting me, of hurting us
And so I left without looking back
We were toxic together, we needed time apart
despite our cravings for more, despite our
magnetic attraction to one another
We needed to grow separately, to grow apart
It was the only way both of us would ever survive

November 20th ~

When he is there, not just providing love but guarding your heart, and providing stillness to your mind; your world feels peaceful and aligned. Both sacrifice parts of themselves to make the other whole. Picking up the pieces, fitting them back in with love, making a masterpiece of both broken but intertwined souls.

November 21st ~

Life without passion is a life void of living fully. I want to be perched on a chair with my toes on your lap. I want your hand caressing my legs and your lips on my knees - sweetly kissing me. I want my hand on the back of your neck as I gently brush my cheek on the top of your head. I want to feel the love that you have for me through every touch, absorbing it into my soul. I want you to know I love you with every ounce of my being without any words being spoken. I want you to feel it through every touch, every kiss, every look and just know.

November 22nd ~

I want all of you ~ every part. Your soul, your body, your mind, your heart, and your love. I won't settle for just a piece. I knew from the very beginning that I would need all of you, want all of you, and deeply desire all of you. If you are not willing, I know I must go ~

How is it that with one word, one phrase, one message - you have me hooked all over again? The moment self-doubt was creeping in due to outside factors that I had no control over, I heard your voice. I heard your words. I heard you say never stop being me - to never stop writing and being open and raw. To never stop being honest and authentic. You tell me, "Keep going with this girl," especially when I am in a zone and my energy matches my words. You tell me that I am writing some of the best things I ever have. And as I sit, listening to your message, I sit teary-eyed because it is exactly what I need to hear right now. You don't know how your message affected me, and you aren't aware of what transpired this morning and how I needed to hear your voice so very much.

November 23rd ~

I will make sure you know how much I cherish who you are every day. I will endlessly kiss your soul and love your heart. I will love your darkness, your radiating light, the parts of your soul you share with others, and the parts you keep deeply hidden, the ones I only know. We will walk together in this life, acknowledging our unexplainable connection and fully accepting one another for who we truly are. Forever painting our dreams alive in the most brilliant colors.
Colors others cannot even fathom.

November 24th ~

I will fly effortlessly
with you in the light
If you sit in despair
with me in the darkness

November 25th ~

One word
one touch
one thought
of what is to come
sets my skin on fire
Feeling you even before
you make physical contact
Our connection
speaks for itself
Immense
Explosive
Unbreakable

November 26th ~

The moment finally arrived one chilly November night. Elation spilled out every one of my pores as I got closer. Butterflies fluttered around my stomach as chills ran down my spine. I was nervous to see you after so many months apart, anticipating your touch. My mind was only filled with longing until now.

Thoughts of your soft lips pressed against mine were blissfully painful. Thoughts of our bodies parting, connecting, and wet with excitement were welcomed. Our eyes locked instantly as you took my hand, leading me over the threshold. I was left wondering what you had in store for my aching body.

Our chemistry exploded as your fingertips gently traced the side of my body, pushing my sweater aside, unbuttoning my dress slowly, and reacquainting yourself with my curves. Red lips, red lace, your favorite color. I surrendered myself to you completely and willingly.

At this moment, I was all yours.

November 27th ~ Red

Your breath lingers on my skin
Invisible now are the places
you once touched
forever etched into memory
The moment is still there in my mind
as I ache for more of what we once had ~
remembering your smell, your gaze, your eyes
The world ceased to exist
outside of you at that moment
even in a crowded place
my thoughts were focused on you
The intensity of that day I long for
thought about, and in an instant
back to normalcy and the life I know
Flashes of you sneak up suddenly
are invited and welcomed even
always replaying in mind
Feeling you dance across
my skin if only through my thoughts
as a memory, and reality no more

November 28th ~

I am a lot of things. However, I am not a damsel in distress or a coward that avoids danger. After years of hidden trauma, I have developed the most ingrained instincts within my soul. Even in the presence of the littlest bit of hysteria, my body is alarmed and ready to fight or flee. Mostly fight. If you are not willing to indulge temptations within the darkness of the devil, confront a romantic, charming siren; or challenge an exquisite, intelligent woman while satiating your innermost cravings of hidden vices, resist the need for me.

I will push your boundaries and test your patience, but please know my motives will always be pure, and my love for you will never fade. I will help you discover parts of yourself, the authentic soul you yearned for ~ never knew but always inherently wanted.

November 29th ~

Make damn sure his mouth follows through with every sensual, dirty thing he promised you throughout the day. Even if dinner must be made, you become the appetizer, satiating every desire uttered from his sexy ass lips.

November 30th ~

Love exiled
by inaction
Tears flooding
regretfully
Watching me
walk away
Realizing now
you're just too late

December 1st ~

Staring deeply into my eyes and you asked me one
question, "Do you trust me?"

I am rarely caught off guard, but you put me on edge,
blissfully causing frisson racing through my body with one
touch of your hand. Of course, I trust him ~ I think to
myself. I know this with every morsel of my soul. I trust this
man with my life. There is no one else I would submit to,
no one else I would let touch my body in ways he only
does, no one else I would let mark my skin, causing such
sweet liberation of self as I gift myself over to him to be
bound; offering up complete control.

I sit before you, staring into your eyes. You tilt my chin to
meet your gaze as I confidently answer, whispering, "Yes,
sir."

December 2nd ~

Anticipation races down my tender inner thigh, mentally envisioning what you have in store for my salacious, wanton body. Unquenched desire drives me mad, but I choose to stay patient, lucid, fully submitting, offering myself to you. Giving up complete control, trusting you to satiate a need deep within me as you whisper sweetly in my ear. My breathing quickens, revealing lascivious desires and lustful glares without breaking eye contact. Waiting. Following. Anticipating. Reveling in the excitement of your execution, the masterpiece before you that is being painted between us. Following directives, being guided safely and gently ~ while I bask in the liberation of self; with you, the artist ~ inducing pleasures and release. Stroke by rough stroke as you see fit.

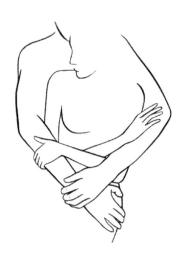

December 3rd ~

So, I see you want to rub my body just the right way
as you seductively poured ink out on paper today
Is that what's desired? ~ That's what you clearly said
Wanting to take me promptly to your sinful, wicked bed?
To taunt, to lick, to eat, to feast,
marking my sweet ass like a feral beast
Did you think I would pass? Not be tempted, be scared?
Our conversations lit my soul ~ to be fully prepared
I'll raise your lustful bet and declare if we met
I no doubt would be calling and ready and wet
After talking and tasting, I feel you would pay
because you would fall smitten more by each day
Seeing my wrists wrapped tightly in ties
the beauty of it all would make you delightfully sigh
You often utter, sweet nothings in French
as you close in to satiate your never-ending quench
Your hand inching up smooth inner thigh
the taste, my scent will have you fucking flying high
But who will be in charge
because your submissive addiction
is also very alpha ~ that's just my prediction
You have no idea what you actually stumbled into
This friendship, our talks, I don't have a clue too
You'll be begging for more by each passing minute
To play, to talk, to fuck, to touch
What will be your ultimate . . . get off?
All I think about is how you would spread me open wide
of all the places your twisting tongue would reside
Connection is needed for me to let you in
to be close enough to touch my tender, soft skin
Such holes we would fall through,

what spells we would brew
I, simply at this moment, can't get enough of you
For now, I'll just let my imagination run wild
while you paint, from afar, to put it safely mild
C'est la vie ~ but please confidently know
you, made this girl eternally smile

December 4th ~

He took me gently to the edge of my limits, pushed my perceived boundaries, and crossed the established borders to show me what life really has to offer ~ gifting me pleasures to experience, pleasures that were unknown before now. In turn, he allowed me to find my true self, presenting just the right amount of fear to guide me out of my comfort zone, learning to shine in the spotlight that was always meant for me from the beginning.

December 5th ~

I don't want a night full of vanilla or strawberry. I want a night full of you, wicked and dark. I want a night full of roughness and passion. I want a night full of pushing limits. I want a night full of you face down on the bed. I want a night full of your trusted submission with my earned dominance ~ exerting control of such a powerful, enchanting woman. A night full of just enough softness in our touch, my lips traveling down your spine, caressing the back of your shoulder, on one another; and in contrast, when the desire for softness is satiated, I want a night full of the harsh sting of my hand against your backside leaving us both weak, exhausted insatiable for more to come.

December 6th ~

Enter me slowly, pausing, soaking in every moment, as you look into my eyes, wanting me ~ and only me tonight. I move my hips slowly, circling, swirling with pleasures in the sensual stillness, feeling the weight of you against me, the brilliance of the lighted view reflecting within my eyes, the wetness between my legs, and a romantic starlit sultry serenade unfolding as you passionately release, filling me. I feel you throb deeply within; a culmination, a climax, the feelings between us, and simply enjoying the pleasure ~ of you.

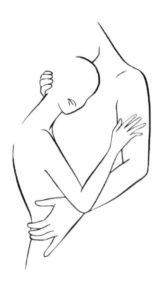

December 7th ~

Our hands touched, and our eyes locked; electricity raced rapidly through our bodies, our souls catching on fire quite quickly. We knew there would be holes to fall through, dragons to slay, hidden time to steal, and battles to be conquered just for sacred seconds together.

Committed we became, and every moment was worth the fight, worth every danger we faced, and validated our longing. You became my Achilles heel, a weakness I cannot resist, a surprise I could not have predicted.

We have accepted each other, accepted our fate, and we are together at long last, knowing even if we begin to fall or stumble, our time has been sealed eternal. We have ruined our ideals of love for anyone else. For there could be no other to replace the spaces you have carved out for yourself in my heart, in my soul.

You are my sweetest downfall, and I loved you first unconditionally ~ forever.

December 8th ~

I need a man with desire in his eyes, romance in his veins, and a firm hand to take what is his. I need a man who is unafraid to grab my face, kiss my tender, innocent lips, and show me who is truly in charge. I need to feel every sensation wash over my body with one look, one touch of his artistic hand painting his way across my skin.

December 9th ~

His fingertips began caressing my left inner thigh under the table as he looked intensely into my golden hazel eyes. Neither of us blinked, connecting in such an intense, fervent way, even in a room full of people. We did not need to say anything at that moment ~ our bodies said it all.

December 10th ~

Give it to me rough
Do not hold back
I am not a fragile fledging
for I am a brilliant butterfly
Strong against the wind
morphing into what you desire
while being true to myself
Not scared of a little pain
for pain brings burning pleasure
Trust between us is deep
and all-encompassing
for I trust you completely
to take me down deep
pleasurable, rabbit holes
while holding my heart
in your hands

December 11th ~

If it carries you away
or you desire it to be so
deep within your soul

~ Please go ~

Do not hesitate
Do not think twice
I will already be gone
when you look back
when you begin to second guess

I already have known, I've felt it
I've felt you ~ being carried away
far before you admitted it
even to yourself

December 12th ~

As I enter the room, admiring the view ~ you are studying
my body. Your eyes memorize every line sheathed in lace. I
feel your stare, anticipating your fingers to follow the map
your eyes have carved. Walking closer, you could not hold
out any longer, animalistic desire taking over; feeling
slightly possessed. You take me into your arms, your hands
ruffling my skirt up, and firmly grabbing my ass, finally
noticing what lies beneath the lace, the mask from the day. I
am yours this evening to do with as you, please.

December 13th ~

You played with my body until there was nothing left. My soul snapped like strings roughly played without proper care. Blood cascaded quickly down my back when all I ever wanted was to be loved. You used my kindness and counted on my authenticity until there was nothing left to give, and still, I stayed.

Feeding you from my immortal life, I was never completely whole again after the war you waged. I offered up hidden, scared parts of my soul, which you took without hesitation. Parts that I cannot mend or play or showcase any longer. Parts you took for the purpose of self-promotion.

And in the end,
I sacrificed myself for the small
chance of a happily ever after.

December 14th ~

As you extend your hand to me,
I tightly take hold, knowing it is only for me
for I am the one created, it seems, just for you,
The authentic you, the one I only know
Choosing to walk with you
grow with you, guided by you
through the darkness
through the forbidden journey
that lays ahead
discovering who we truly are together
never letting go of your hand,
the hand you extended blindly to me
from the beginning long ago
with the feeling of finally finding
our true place with each other

December 15th ~

I want to be your number one. I want to know I'm the only
one that matters romantically. I will concede one hundred
percent of the time. If there are other options, self-
sacrificing myself, my happiness, for yours ~ without a
doubt, always. I am a fighter, but not when it comes to my
heart. It is easier to let go of what is ultimately not meant
for me.

December 16th ~

After having your way with me, pretending to be a wounded, frightened lamb, and satiating yourself with my sweet nectar after a successful seduction by your true self, the hidden wolf, you further tempted me down a dark, narrow, never-ending seedy hole, for your pleasure. You continued to drop breadcrumbs of truth and attention, knowing I would readily scoop them up, always wanting more of you in any way possible.

I recognized your abase and gratuitous behavior, but I was unable to abdicate my responsibility. I needed to see this through. To find my own way out and rid myself of you for good. So I continued on this journey, conquering these trials you set forth until I could fly, breaking your spell and rising out into the unknown, abandoning you forever, realizing I never needed you to begin with ~

I held the magic all along; the magic you sought out and didn't want to lose but didn't quite know how to harness it, to fully control it, control me. You destroyed yourself in the process of me finding belief in myself.

<u>December 17th ~</u>

Your silence speaks volumes
No words are needed
to convey your ultimate truth
Your silence becomes an untold story
a missed opportunity
a risk you were not willing to take
Perhaps a deep rabbit hole
you were not brave enough
to explore, just yet
And so, there is no other option left
but ~ to let you go, to fly
to navigate your truth
without me

December 18th ~

I heard you were expecting me. Expecting me to do what exactly? Expecting me to be your pawn? For me to be here for your pleasure? Expecting me to follow your commands? You should, perhaps, expect me to put you in your place. I am not a pawn; I am your queen, and you, my dear boy, will bow down before me and take it like a man. It is now too late. I have stopped rhyming to your rhythm, inspired by your soul, and now I fully believe in myself ~ without you.

At this moment with you, now and not forever,
I believe, everything becomes inescapable
The freedom of myself, and mine alone
beyond all measure or reason,
thoughts that breed insanity
I think I am terrified to understand
inhibitions that are continuously mounting
recognizing you becoming pure obsession
The thought of love without actually knowing
controlled, exact, precise, precision occurring
They say only two circumstances are present
when a person disregards the rules of society,
committing a crime or when people are in love
Well, I was in love, but I finally realized
that I never actually needed you to begin with

December 19th ~

Strip me down to my flaws. Look at every scar on my pristine skin. Study every difficult moment that has touched my body; my soul. Moments I conquered & survived. Moments that forced me to create my world around past heartaches felt, a strength that was needed to rebuild myself time and time again, and desires I felt that have become just out of reach. Please understand I would love you with every ounce of who I am. But ~ I don't need you. I could walk away without looking back. I could never hate you because you linger deeply within my soul. I'll simply just pretend you don't exist.

December 20th ～

The truth behind my transformation has not been pretty. I have bedded snakes and bitten into poisonous apples, and still, I rise.

I have fought with every morsel of my being, persevering through nightmares, never succumbing to doubts and disbelief. I ultimately know I am the writer of my own life, a legend in the making, the infamous, and I am now ready for any challenge set forth before me, setting fire to the once was. Letting it all burn, the ash and apprehension dissipating with the wind.

And so I go to create my legacy, relish in the spotlight, and learn that I can be anything and everything I have ever dreamed of. I am ready to soar. I am ready to become myself, the mask destroyed and thrown aside. The impostor respectfully decides to sit this one out but is smiling in the background, immensely proud of the brave woman she helped birth, nurture, and create.

Afterthought ~

"I hate you," I managed to say with a smirk spreading across my face.
"That's a lie," he quickly responded via text.
"I wish it weren't," I said, in a moment of fake honesty.
"That's . . . another lie," he typed back.
And damn ~ he was right.

For years now, I couldn't ever hate him. For years now, I still can't wait until the next time I see him. For years now, he has become so embedded in my soul. Or perhaps it's just the thought of his lips... because fuck, they're soft and amazing to kiss. They are unforgettable.

He was the first person I ever wrote about. Talk about the pressure of being a first. I'd say that's a first worth it all. To be forever immortalized ~ inked within pages, etched on paper, forever remembered. He will forever be remembered, but separate.

Acknowledgments ~

There are a million words I could write to express my gratitude, but I want to simply (not simply) thank ~ my family, my friends, my mentors, my publisher, my support network, my readers, and my audience from the bottom of my heart.

Thank you for believing in my vision.

Thank you for believing in me and my ideas.

Thank you for giving me the time, love, and support to make this dream a reality.

I've realized in completing this book, that big visions can become big realities, if you have the courage to believe in yourself.

Page 51 "Baby, come on" is a line from 'Sleep on the Floor' by The Lumineers

About the Author ~

I began my journey writing poetry about love and loss. More recently, I have been writing erotic prose, diving into short stories, and working on my first fiction novel. Living right outside the borders of Philadelphia, Pennsylvania, I've had many adventures that have guided my writing. Most are about moments that took place throughout my life that I've changed, mixed with fiction and flair to add allure and excitement for your reading pleasure. I love to take my readers on an emotional journey to experience my world and writings as I do - feeling each word I pen on the pages. But above all, I am a woman who craves what we all do - to be loved and cherished. These are my thoughts, my fantasies, my cravings, and my words, woven together for you to enjoy and love.

Follow me for more.

Website - www.teganmatthews.com
Facebook - Tegan Matthews, Author Page

Printed in Great Britain
by Amazon

43516573R00169